FOR ORGANS, PIANOS & ELECTRONIC KEYBOARDS

E-Z PLAY® TODAY

4

C000174310

MOVIE FAVOURITES

HLE

Hal Leonard Europe

Exclusive Distributors:
Music Sales Limited
8/9 Frith Street,
London W1V 5TZ, England.
Music Sales Pty Limited
120 Rothschild Avenue, Rosebery,
NSW 2018, Australia.

Order No. HLE90000210
ISBN 0-7119-6428-9

Cover design by Pearce Marchbank, Studio Twenty, London
Printed in the USA

Your Guarantee of Quality
As publishers, we strive to produce every book
to the highest commercial standards.
This book has been carefully designed to minimise awkward
page turns and to make playing from it a real pleasure.
Throughout, the printing and binding have been
planned to ensure a sturdy, attractive publication which
should give years of enjoyment.
If your copy fails to meet our high standards,
please inform us and we will gladly replace it.

Music Sales' complete catalogue describes
thousands of titles and is available in full colour
sections by subject, direct from Music Sales Limited.
Please state your areas of interest and send a
cheque/postal order for £1.50 for postage to:
Music Sales Limited, Newmarket Road,
Bury St. Edmunds, Suffolk IP33 3YB, England.

Visit the Internet Music Shop at
http://www.musicsales.co.uk

Beauty and the Beast

from Walt Disney's BEAUTY AND THE BEAST

Registration 1
Rhythm: Pops or 8 Beat

Lyrics by Howard Ashman
Music by Alan Menken

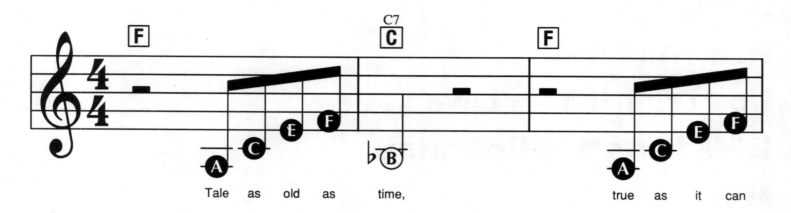

Tale as old as time, true as it can

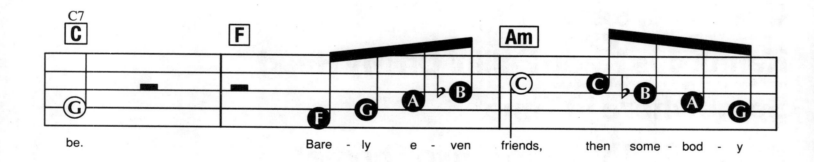

be. Bare - ly e - ven friends, then some - bod - y

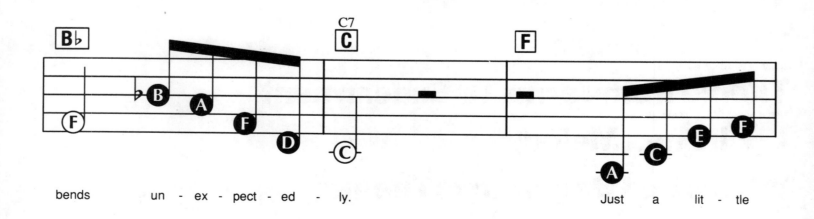

bends un - ex - pect - ed - ly. Just a lit - tle

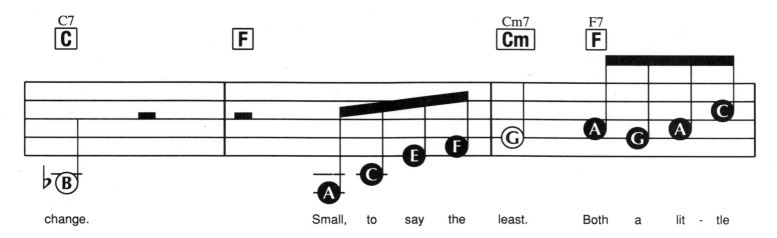

change. Small, to say the least. Both a lit - tle

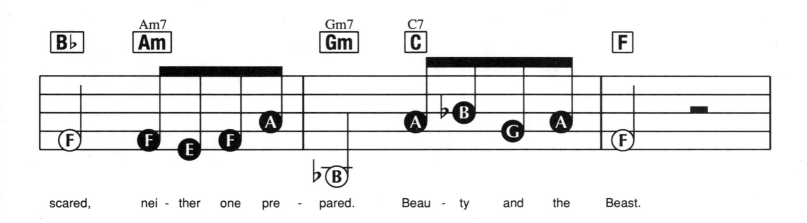

scared, nei - ther one pre - pared. Beau - ty and the Beast.

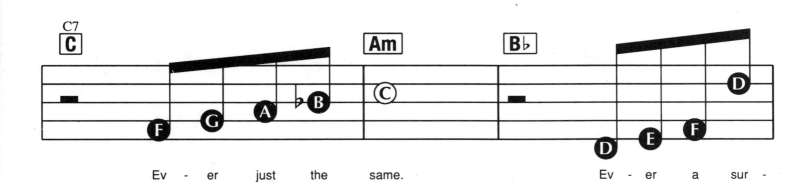

Ev - er just the same. Ev - er a sur -

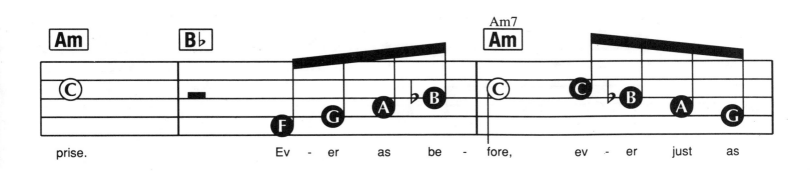

prise. Ev - er as be - fore, ev - er just as

6

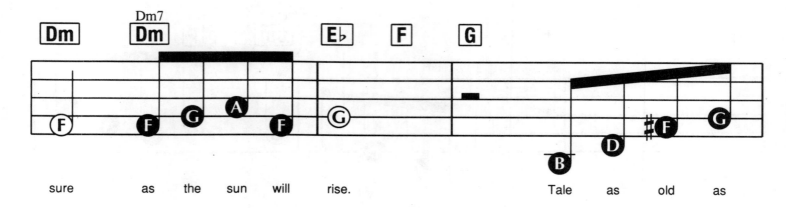

sure   as   the   sun   will   rise.   Tale   as   old   as

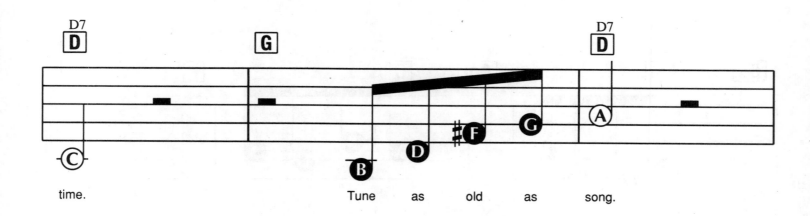

time.   Tune   as   old   as   song.

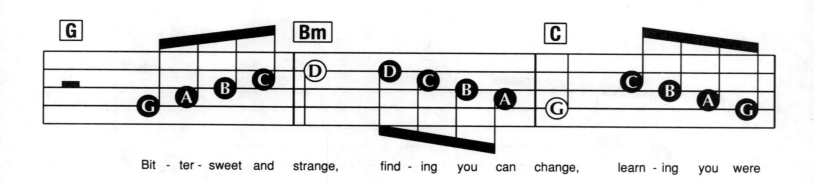

Bit - ter - sweet and   strange,   find - ing   you   can   change,   learn - ing   you   were

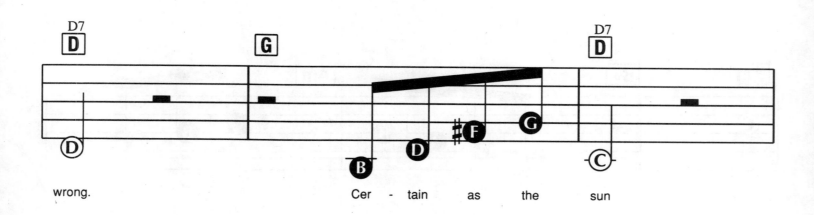

wrong.   Cer - tain   as   the   sun

7

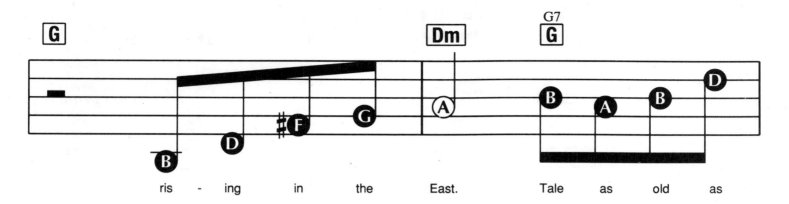

rising in the East. Tale as old as

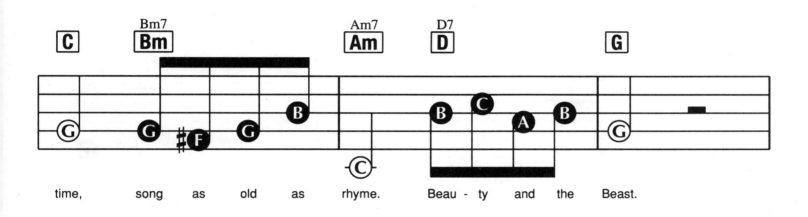

time, song as old as rhyme. Beau - ty and the Beast.

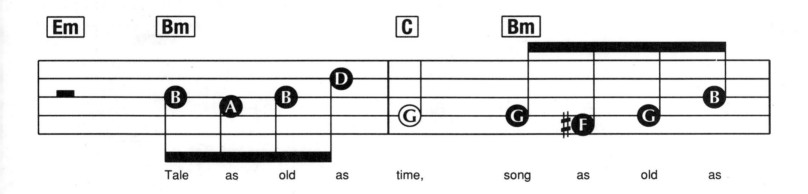

Tale as old as time, song as old as

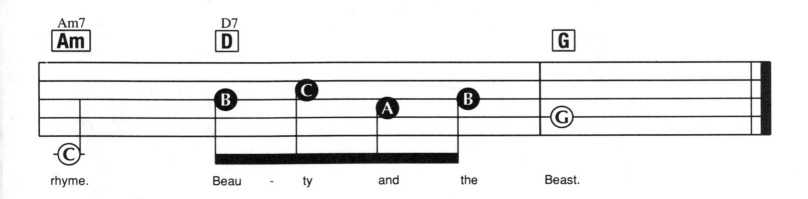

rhyme. Beau - ty and the Beast.

Call Me Irresponsible

from the Paramount Picture PAPA'S DELICATE CONDITION

Registration 7
Rhythm: Swing or Big Band

Words by Sammy Cahn
Music by James Van Heusen

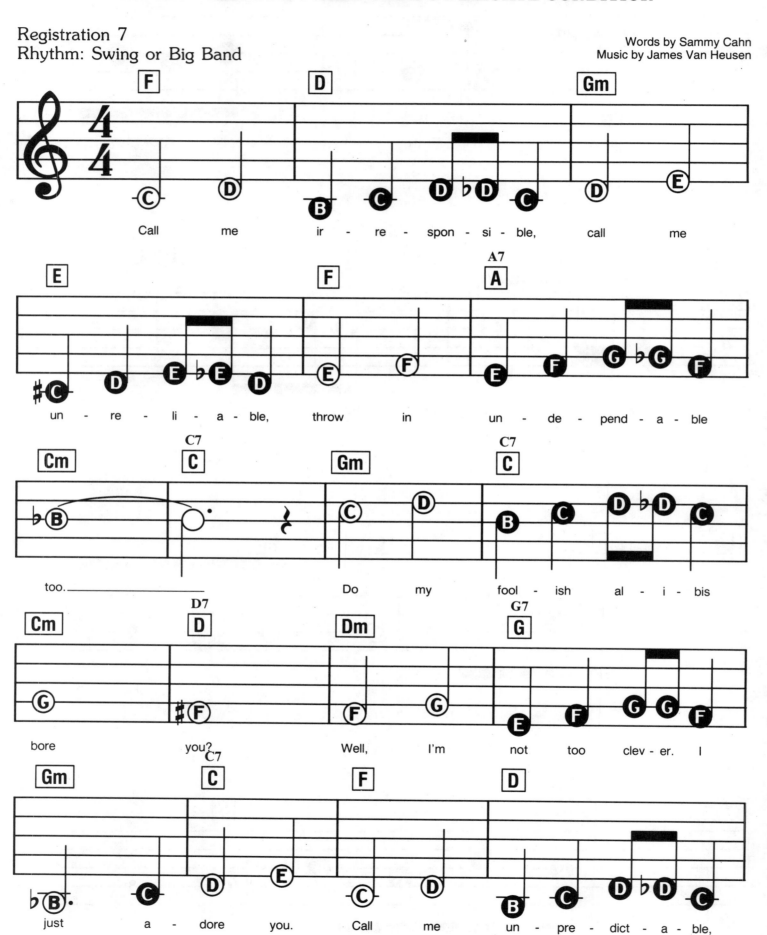

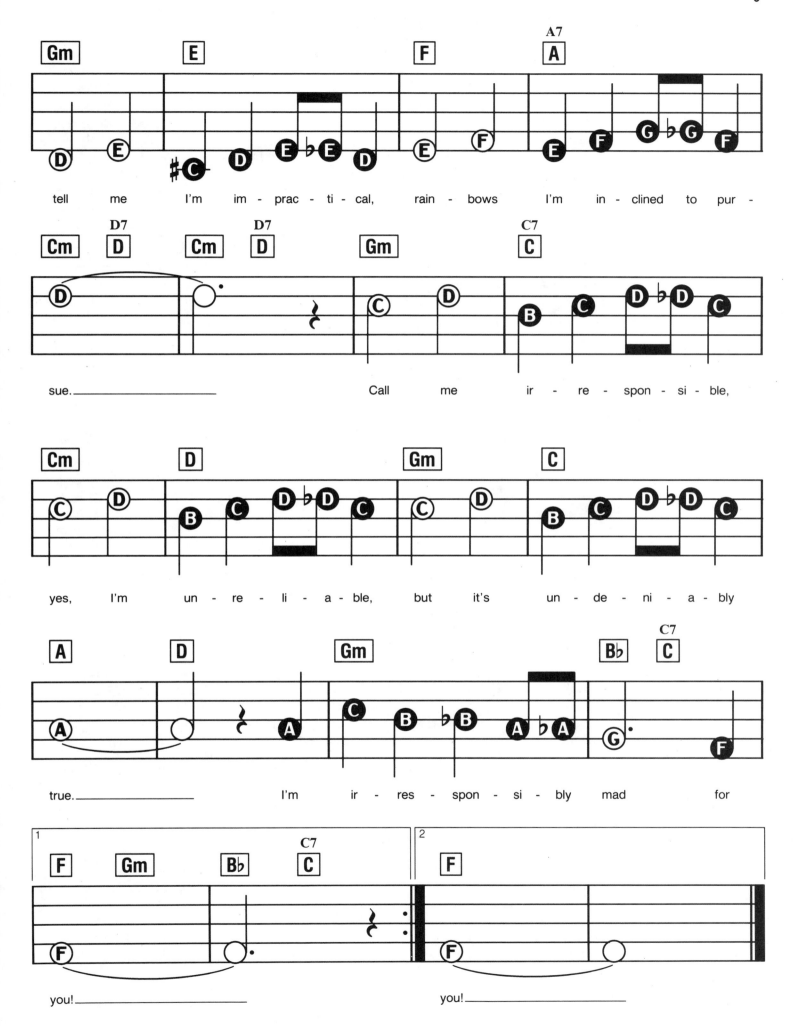

Candle on the Water
from Walt Disney's PETE'S DRAGON

Registration 1
Rhythm: Fox Trot or Ballad

Words and Music by Al Kasha
and Joel Hirschhorn

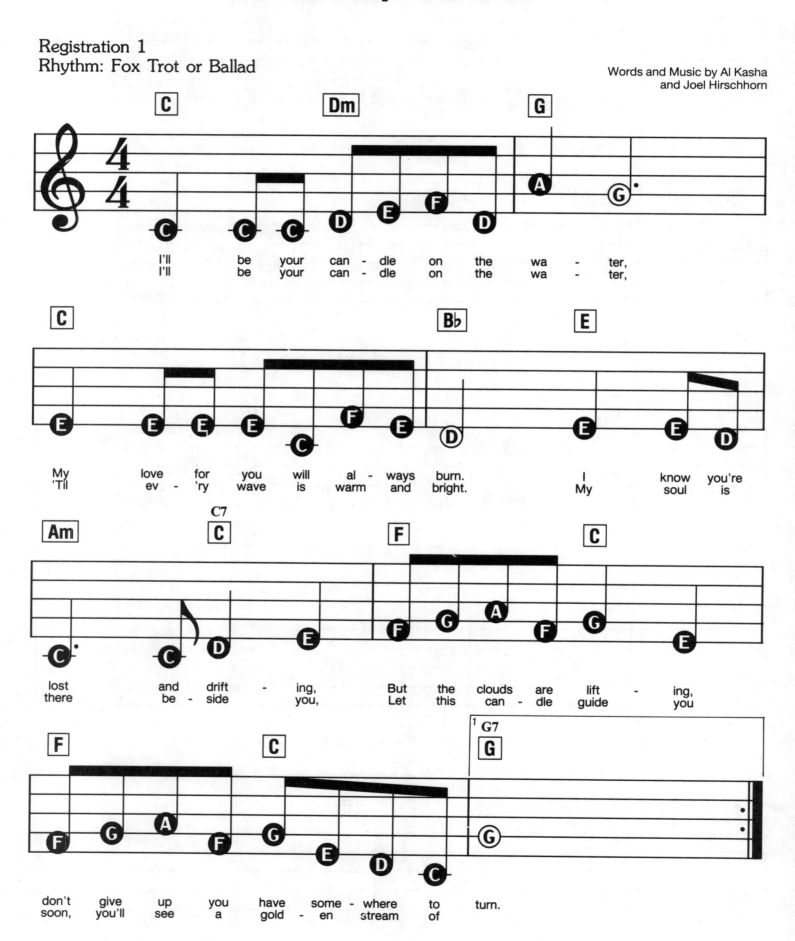

Footloose
Theme from the Paramount Motion Picture FOOTLOOSE

Registration 4
Rhythm: Rock or 8 Beat

Words by Dean Pitchford and Kenny Loggins
Music by Kenny Loggins

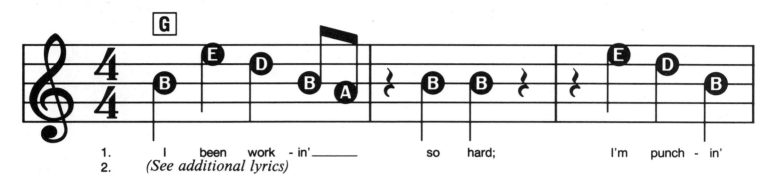

1. I been work - in' so hard; I'm punch - in'
2. *(See additional lyrics)*

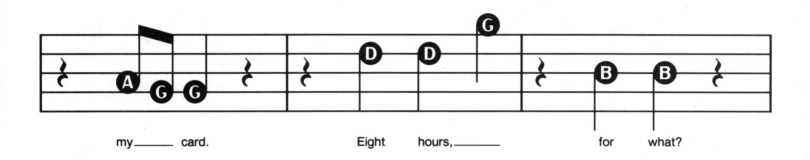

my card. Eight hours, for what?

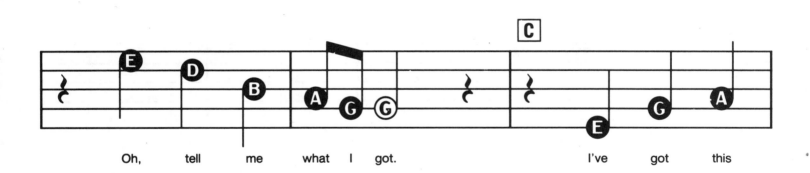

Oh, tell me what I got. I've got this

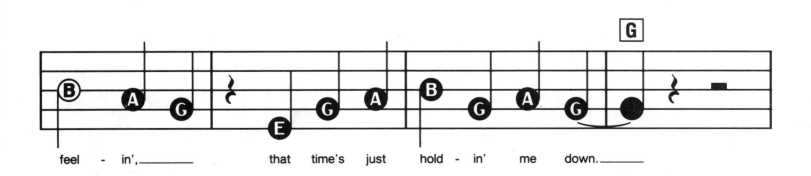

feel - in', that time's just hold - in' me down.

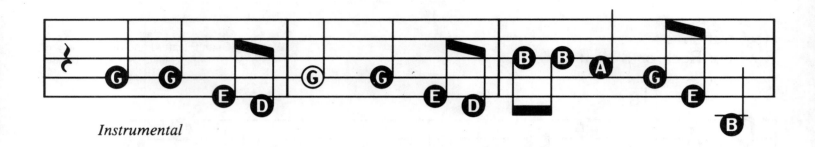

Instrumental

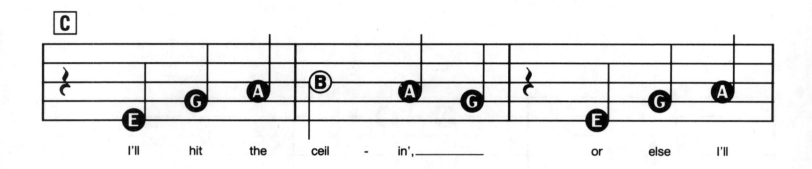

I'll   hit   the   ceil - in',_____   or   else   I'll

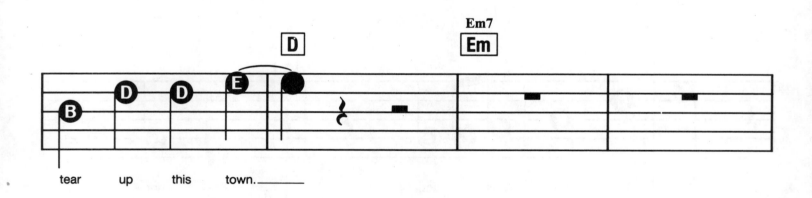

tear   up   this   town._____

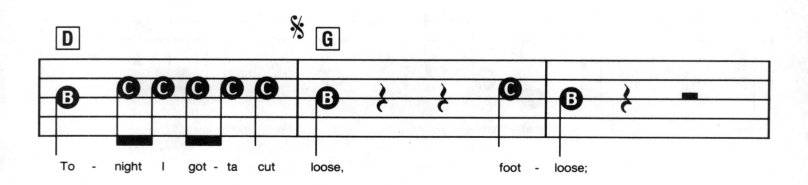

To - night I got - ta cut   loose,   foot - loose;

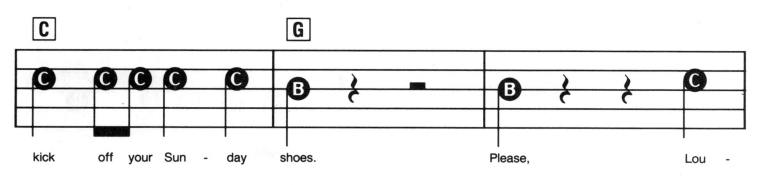

kick off your Sun - day shoes. Please, Lou -

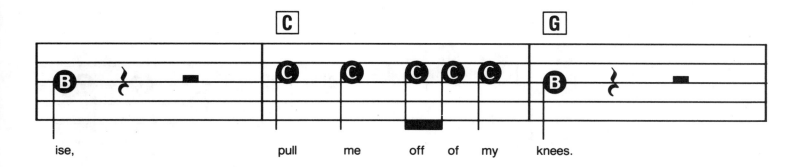

ise, pull me off of my knees.

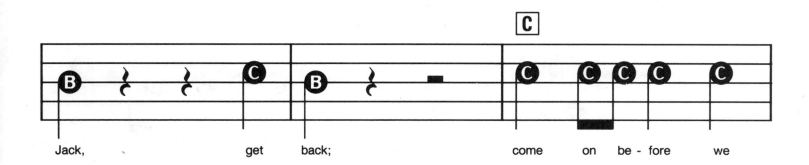

Jack, get back; come on be - fore we

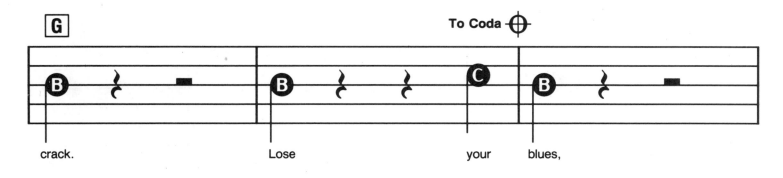

To Coda

crack. Lose your blues,

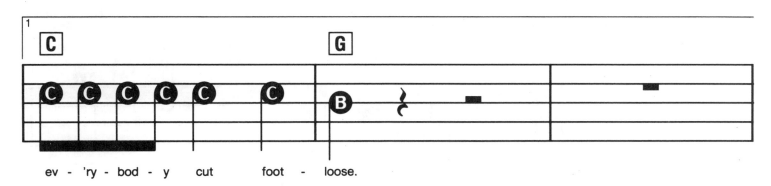

ev - 'ry - bod - y cut foot - loose.

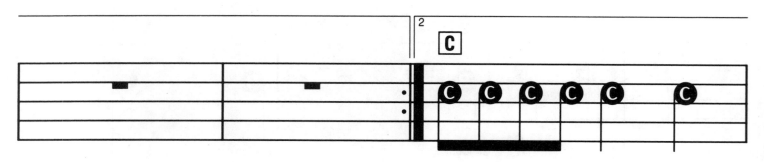

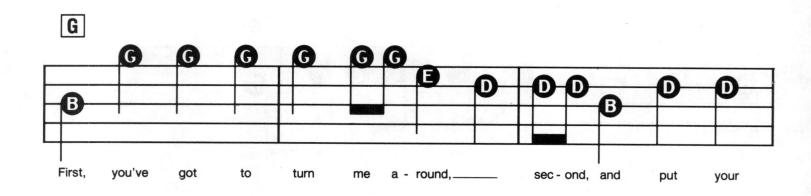

First, you've got to turn me a - round,_____ sec - ond, and put your

feet on the ground._____ Third, now, take a hold of your soul._____

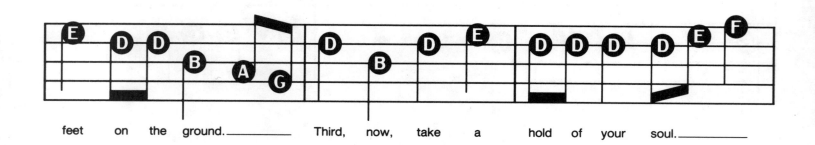

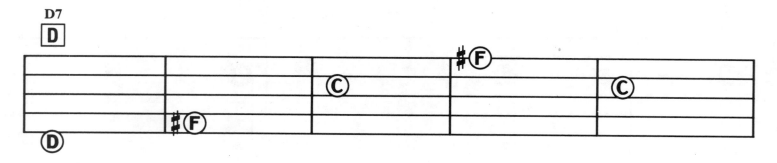

D.S. al Coda
(Return to %
Play to ⊕ and
skip to Coda)

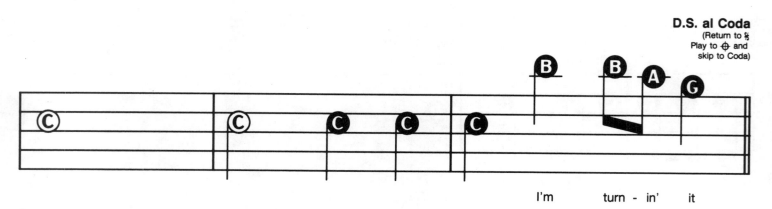

I'm turn - in' it

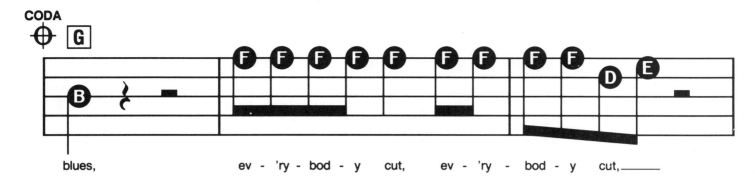

blues,   ev - 'ry - bod - y cut,   ev - 'ry - bod - y cut,_____

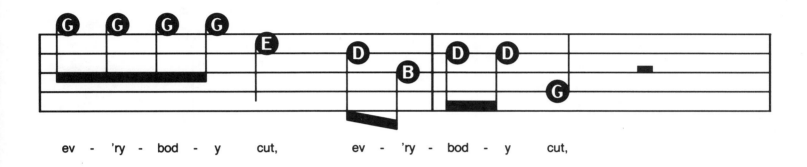

ev - 'ry - bod - y cut,   ev - 'ry - bod - y cut,

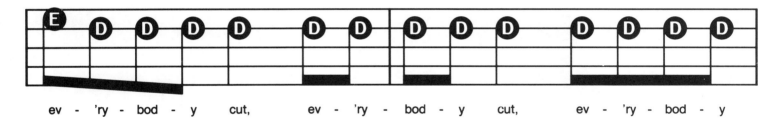

ev - 'ry - bod - y cut,   ev - 'ry - bod - y cut,   ev - 'ry - bod - y

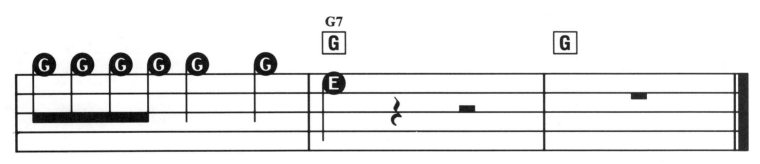

ev - 'ry - bod - y cut foot - loose.

Additional Lyrics

Verse 2:
You're playin' so cool
Obeying every rule
Dig way down in your heart
You're burnin', yearnin' for some...
Somebody to tell you
That life ain't a-passin' you by.
I'm tryin' to tell you
It will if you don't even try;
You can fly if you'd only cut

Chorus:
Loose, footloose,
Kick off your Sunday shoes.
Ooh-ee, Marie,
Shake it, shake it for me.
Whoa, Milo,
Come on, come on let's go.
Lose your blues,
Everybody cut footloose.

A Fine Romance
from SWING TIME

Registration 2
Rhythm: Ballad or Swing

Words by Dorothy Fields
Music by Jerome Kern

A fine ro - mance! With no

kiss - es! A fine ro - mance, My friend,

this is! We should be like a cou - ple of hot to -

ma - toes,_____ But you're as cold as

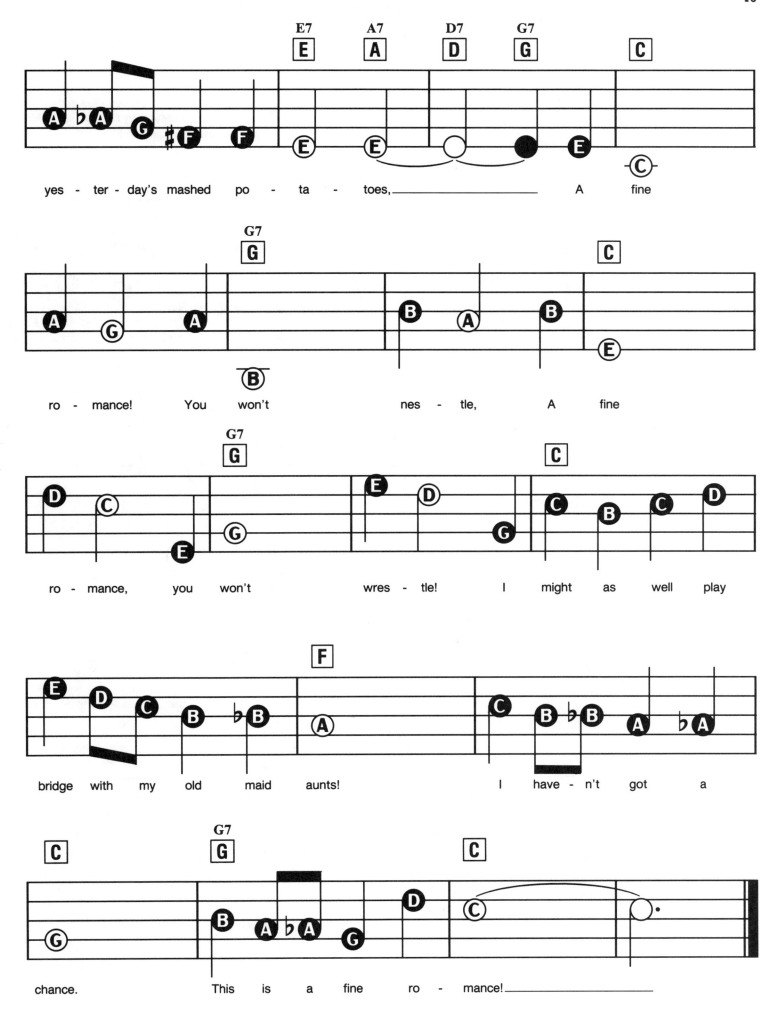

Heart and Soul
from the Paramount Short Subject A SONG IS BORN

Registration 8
Rhythm: Swing

Words by Frank Loesser
Music by Hoagy Carmichael

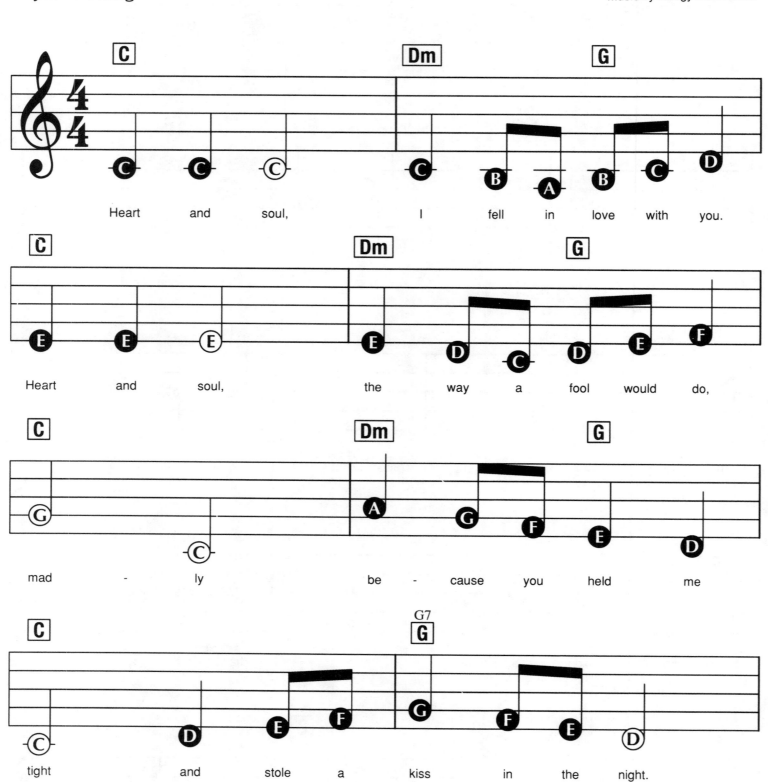

22

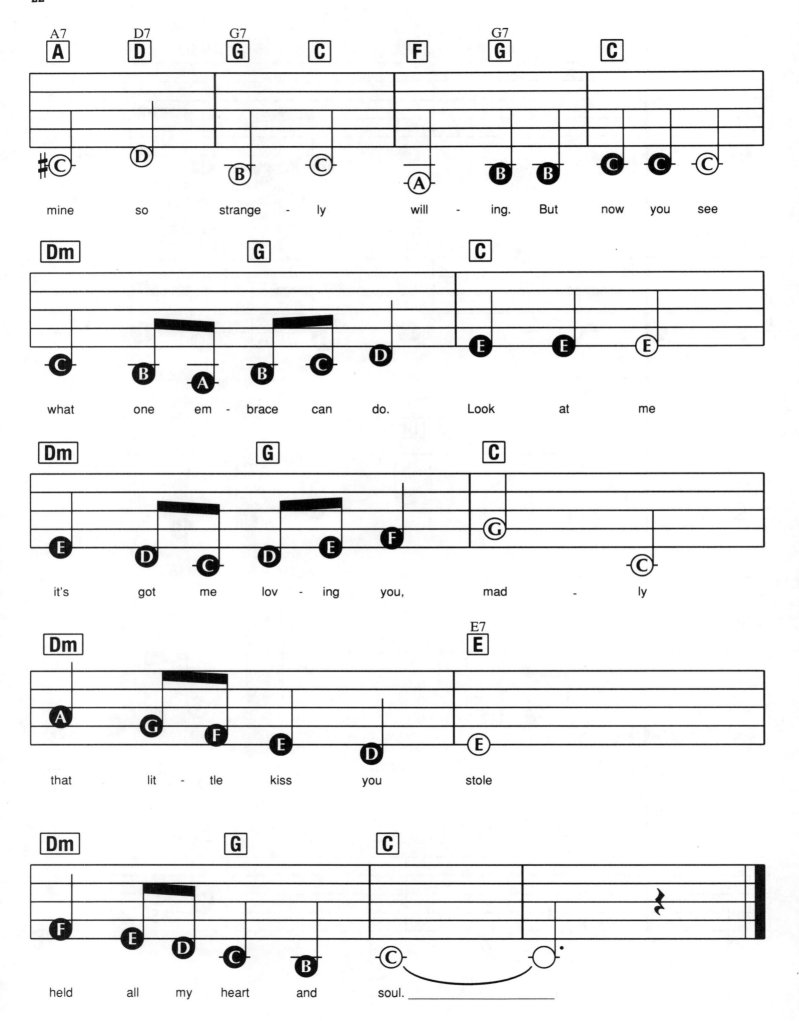

How Deep Is Your Love
from the Motion Picture SATURDAY NIGHT FEVER

Registration 4
Rhythm: Soft Rock or Rock

Words and Music by Barry Gibb,
Maurice Gibb and Robin Gibb

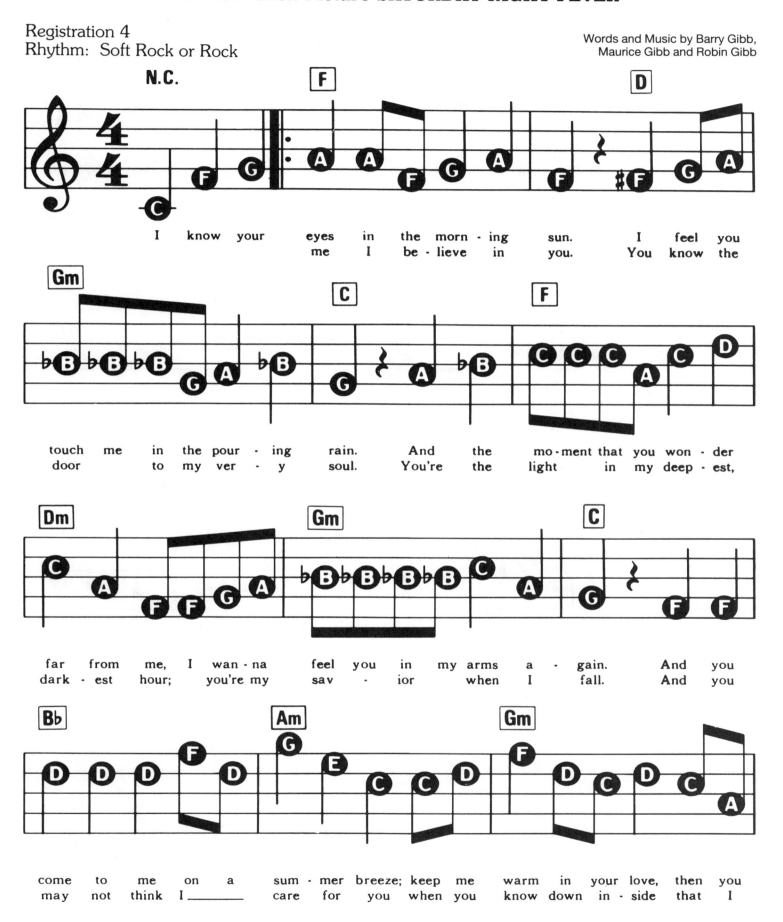

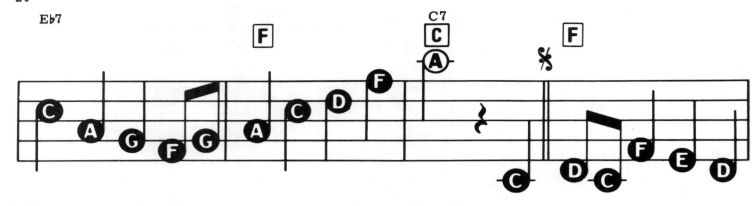

soft - ly leave.
real - ly do. } And it's me you need to show: How deep is your love? How

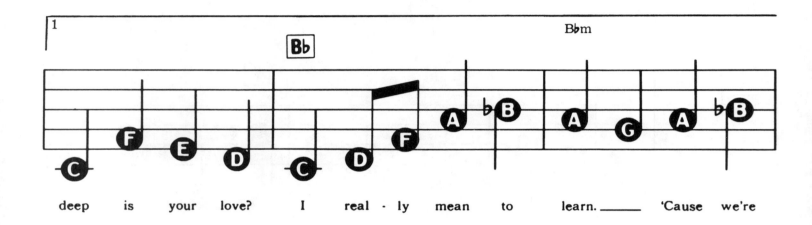

deep is your love? I real - ly mean to learn.____ 'Cause we're

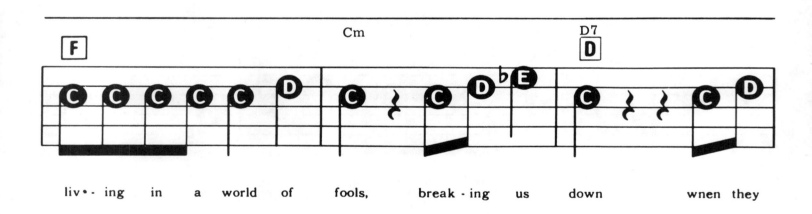

liv - ing in a world of fools, break - ing us down when they

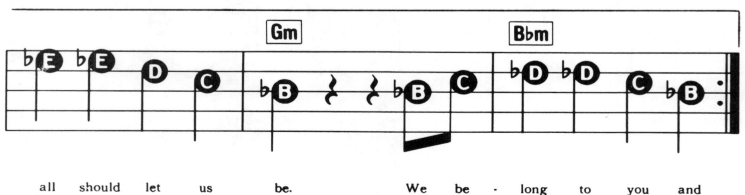

all should let us be. We be - long to you and

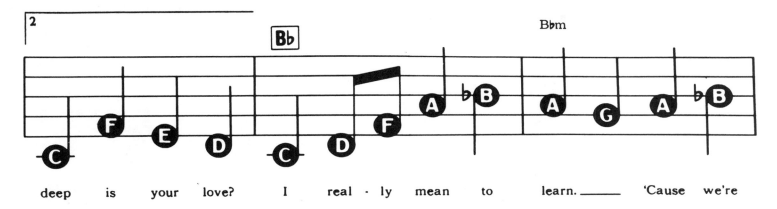

deep   is   your   love?   I   real - ly   mean   to   learn. _____ 'Cause   we're

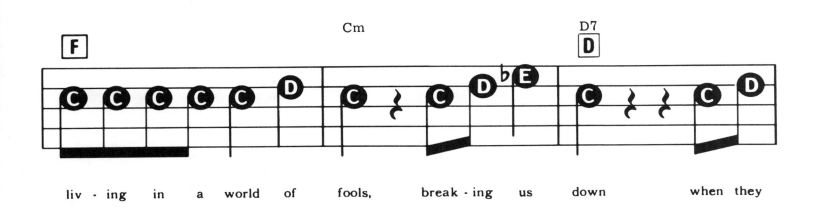

liv - ing   in   a   world   of   fools,   break - ing   us   down   when   they

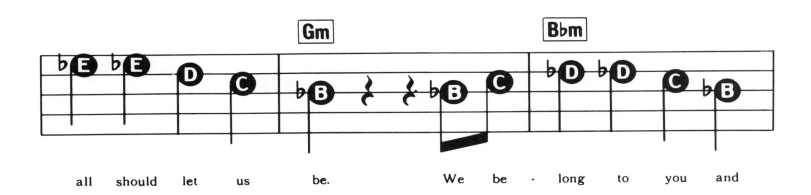

all   should   let   us   be.   We   be - long   to   you   and

D.S. and Fade
(Return to 𝄋
and fade)

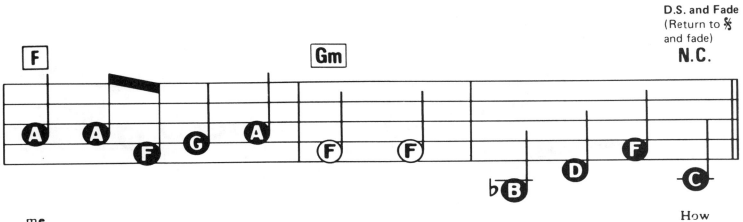

me.   How

It Might as Well Be Spring
from STATE FAIR

Lyrics by Oscar Hammerstein II
Music by Richard Rodgers

Registration 3
Rhythm: Ballad

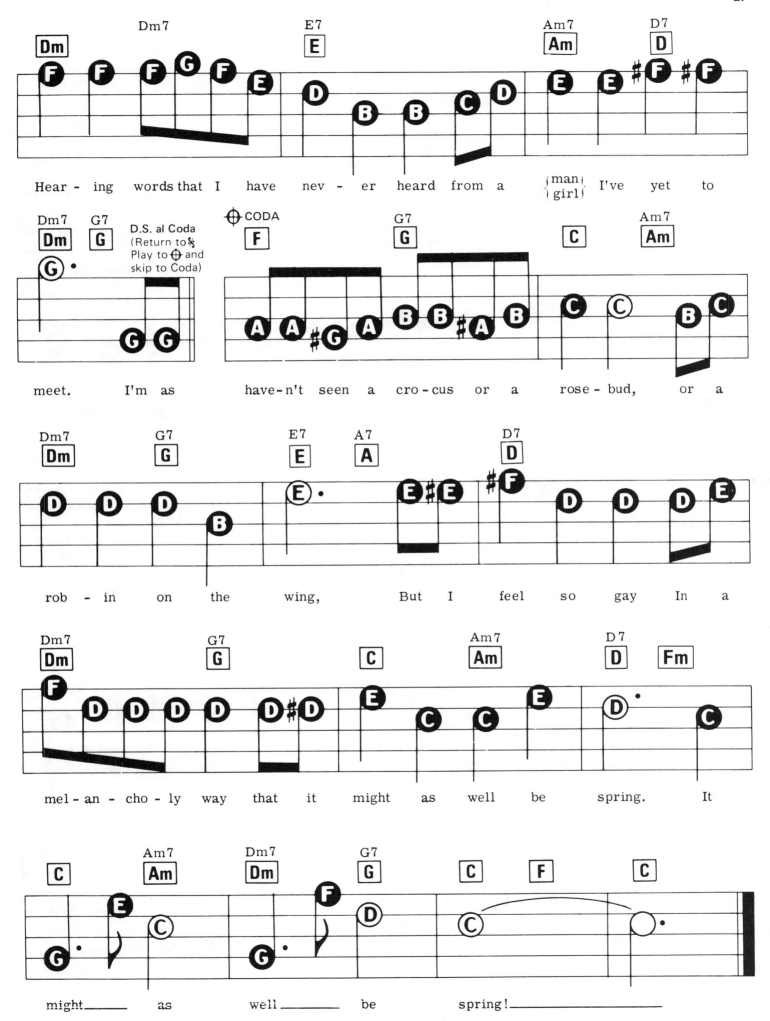

Mona Lisa
from MONA LISA

Registration 9
Rhythm: Swing or 8 Beat

By Jay Livingston
and Ray Evans

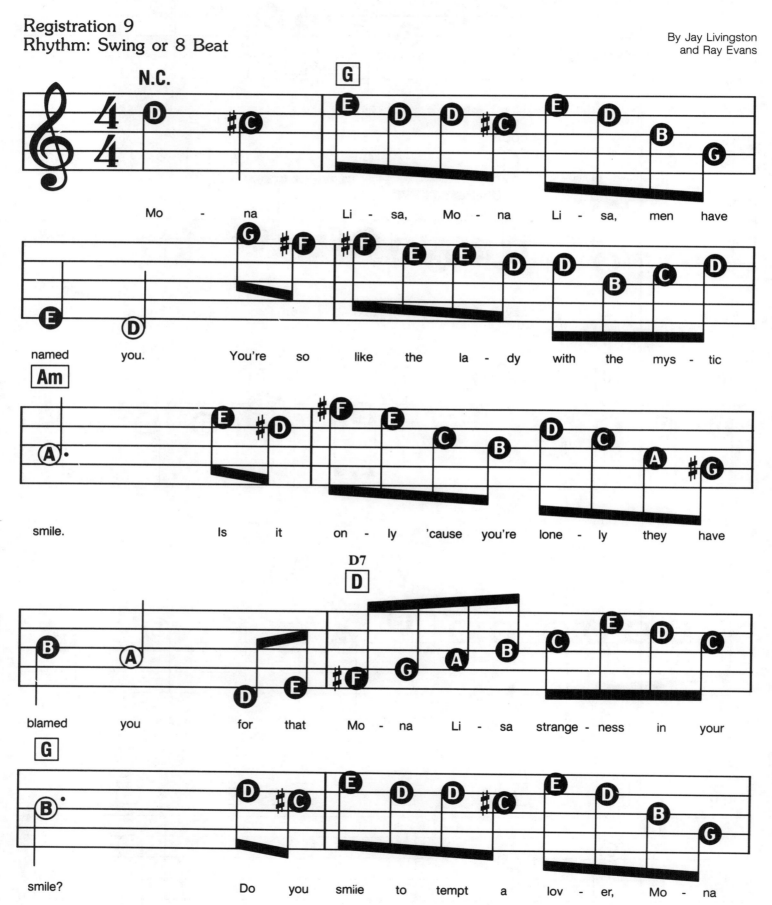

Moonlight Becomes You
from the Paramount Picture ROAD TO MOROCCO

Registration 1
Rhythm: Swing

Words by Johnny Burke
Music by James Van Heusen

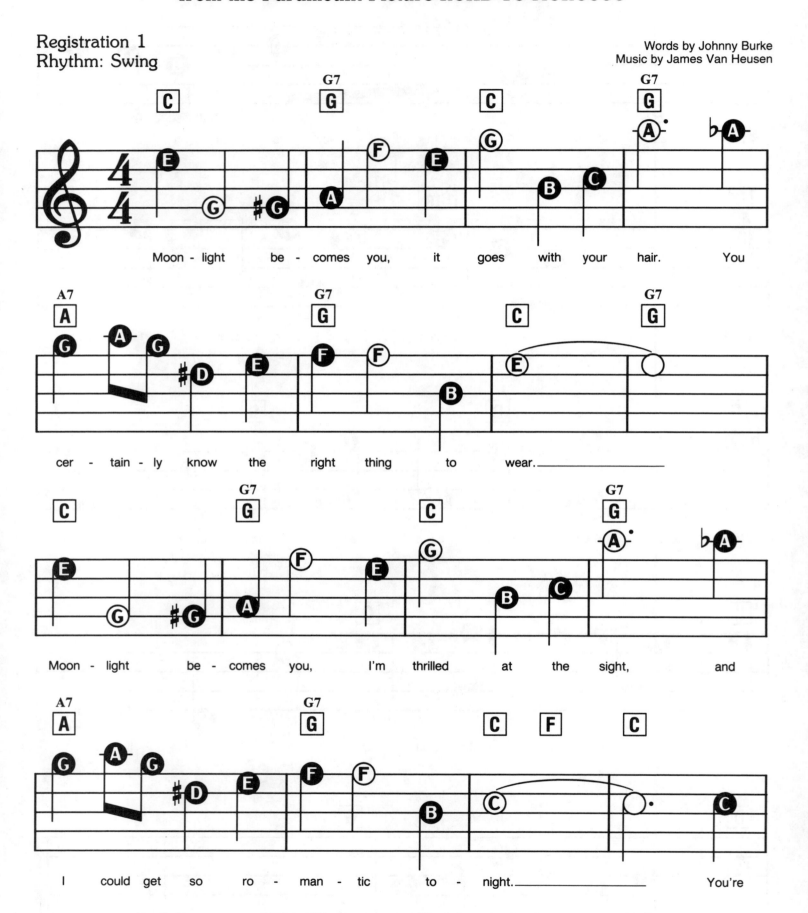

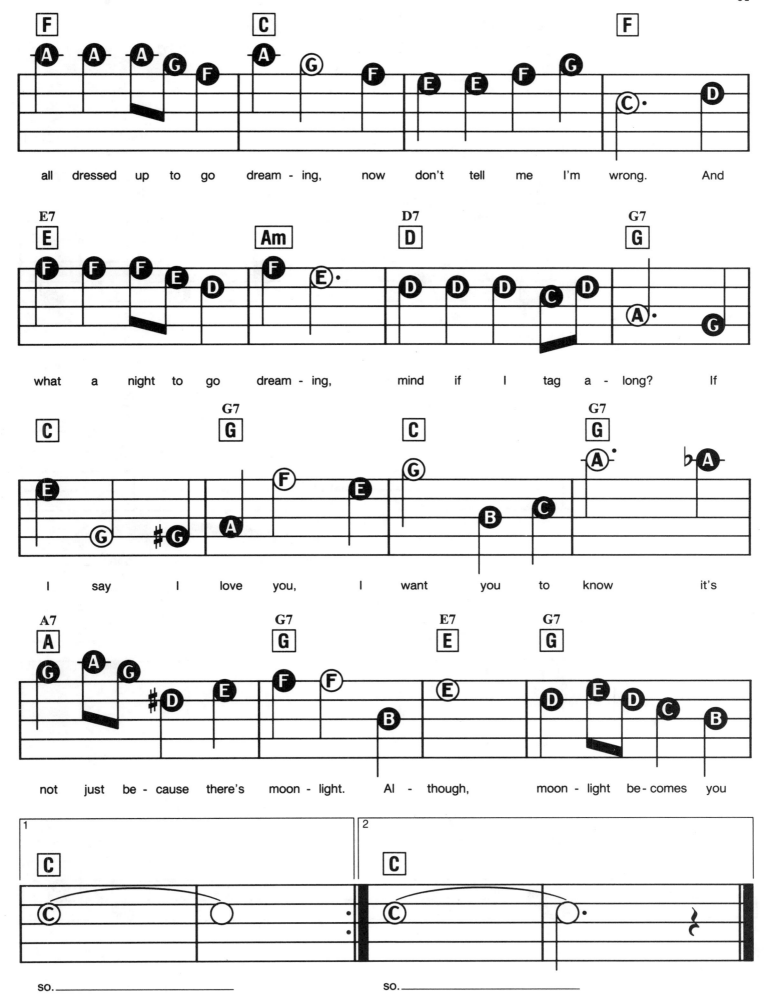

The Odd Couple
Theme from the Paramount Picture THE ODD COUPLE

Registration 5
Rhythm: Shuffle or Swing

Words by Sammy Cahn
Music by Neal Hefti

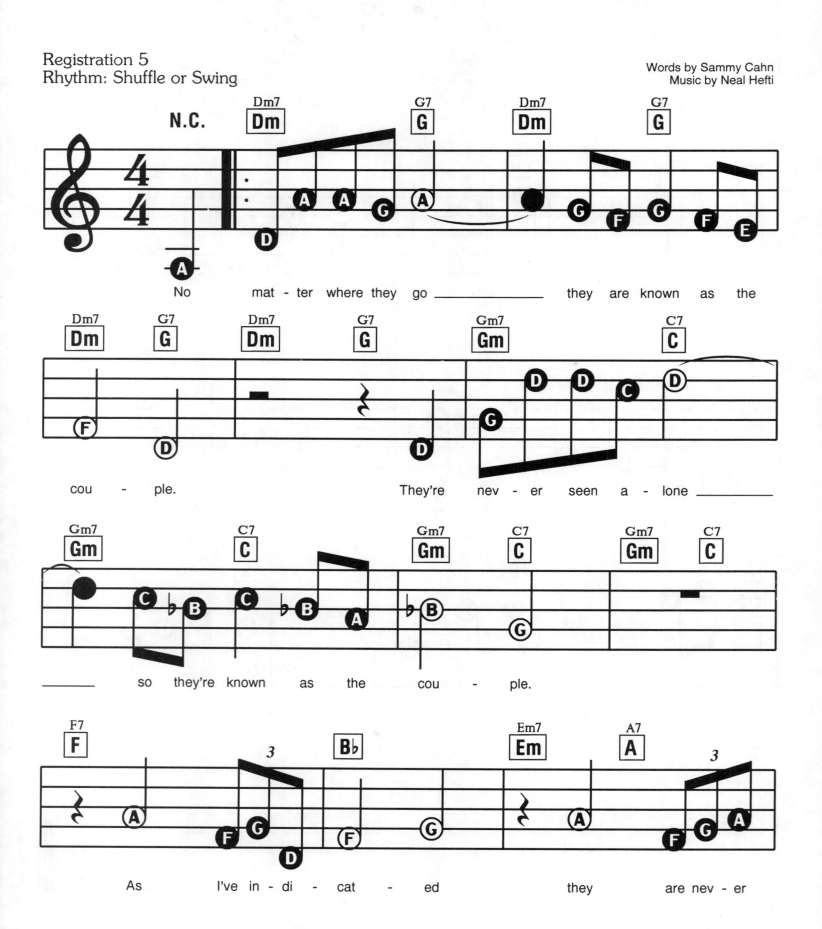

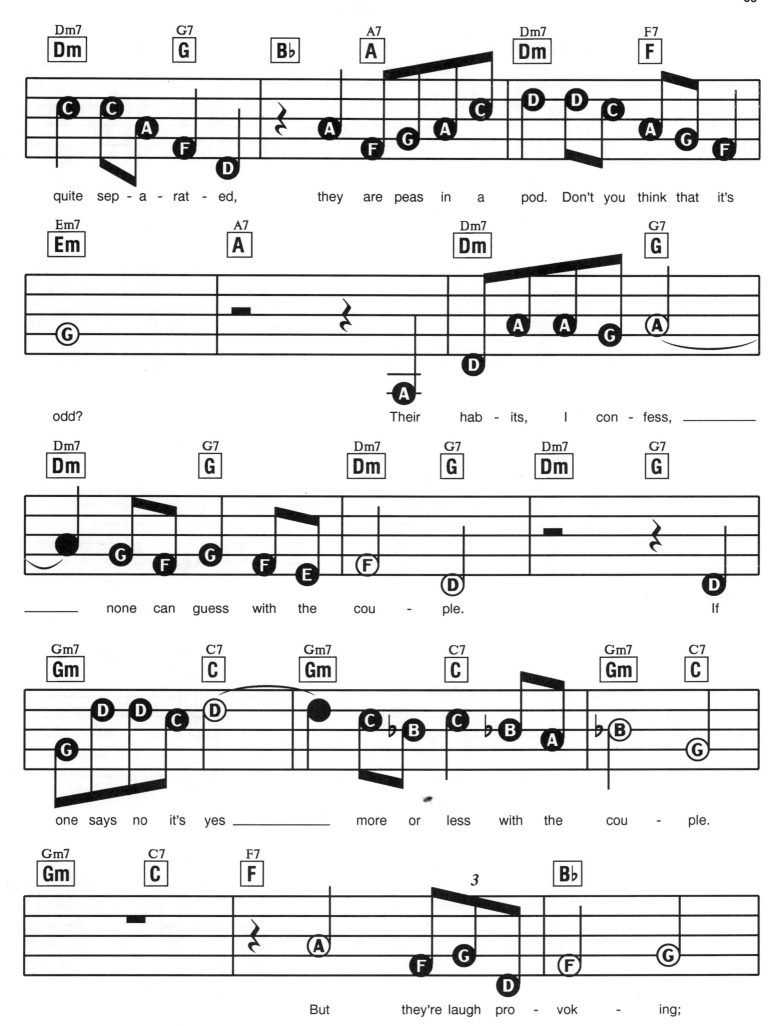

34

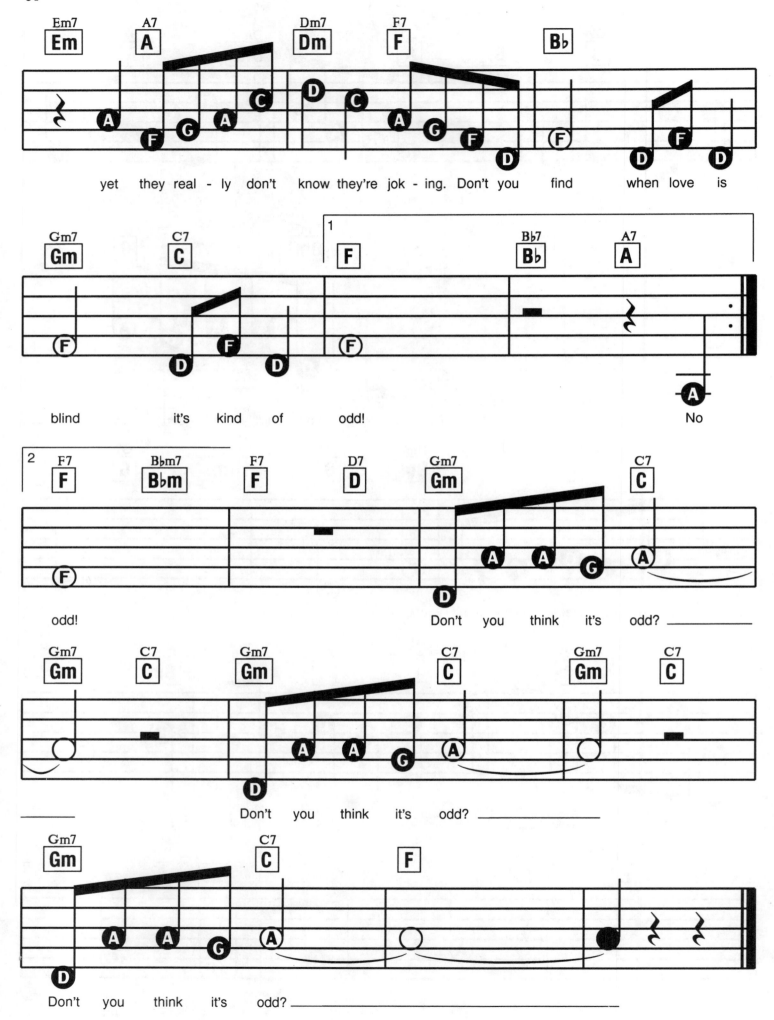

yet they real - ly don't know they're jok - ing. Don't you find when love is

blind it's kind of odd! No

odd! Don't you think it's odd? _____

_____ Don't you think it's odd? _____

Don't you think it's odd? _____

Raindrops Keep Fallin' on My Head

from BUTCH CASSIDY AND THE SUNDANCE KID

Registration 5
Rhythm: Swing or Shuffle

Lyric by Hal David
Music by Burt Bacharach

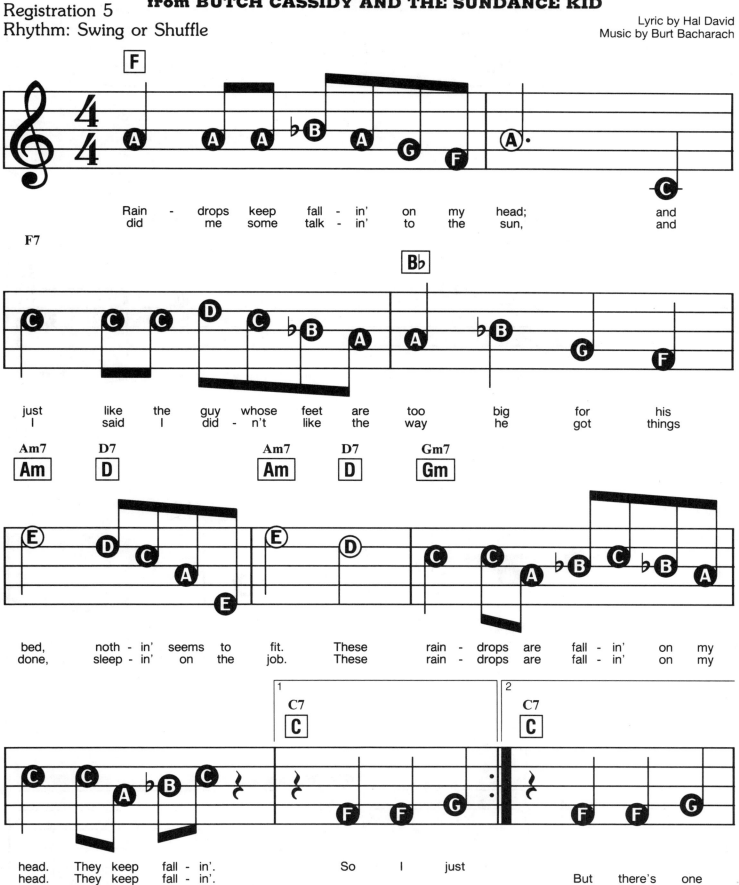

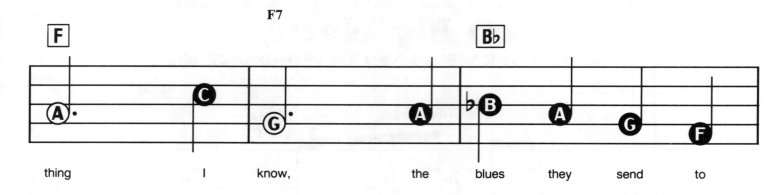

thing   I   know,   the   blues   they   send   to

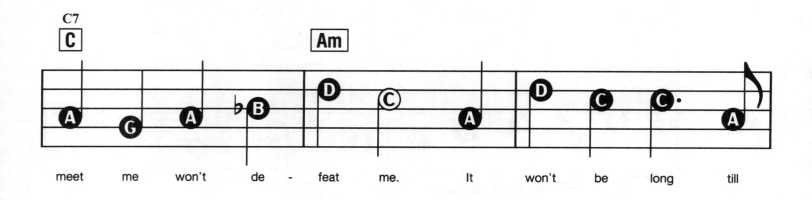

meet   me   won't   de - feat   me.   It   won't   be   long   till

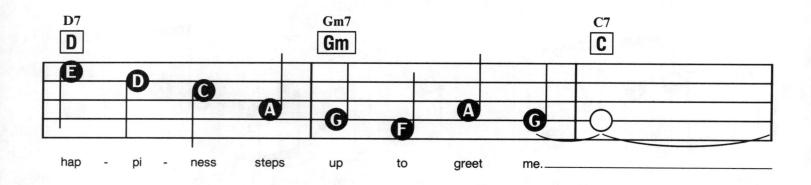

hap - pi - ness   steps   up   to   greet   me._____

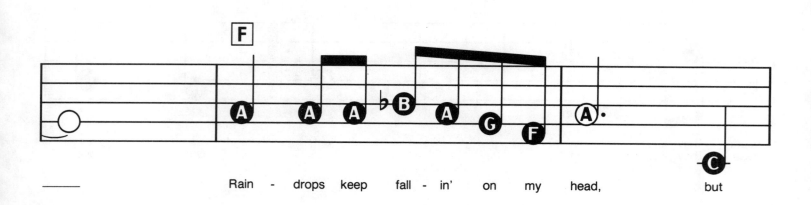

_____   Rain - drops   keep   fall - in'   on   my   head,   but

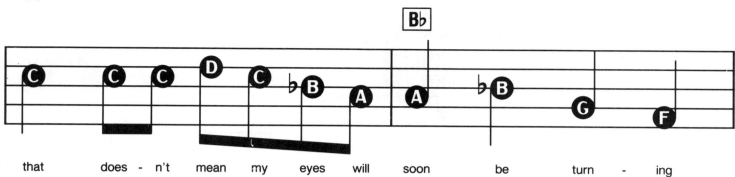

that   does - n't   mean   my   eyes   will   soon   be   turn - ing

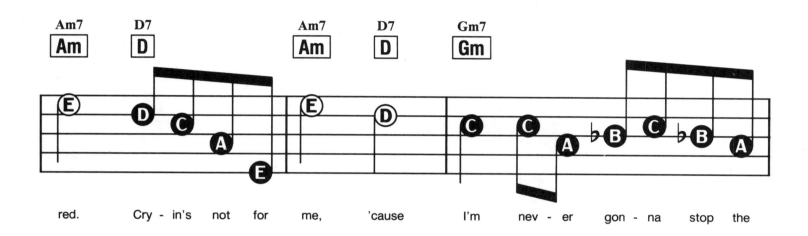

red.   Cry - in's   not   for   me,   'cause   I'm   nev - er   gon - na   stop   the

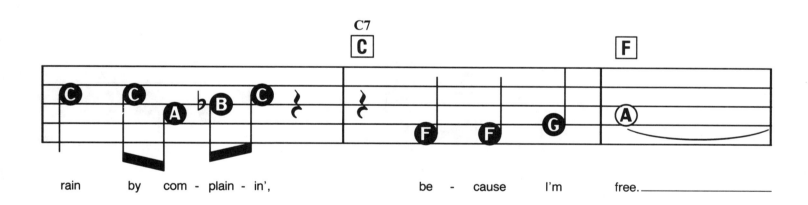

rain   by   com - plain - in',   be - cause   I'm   free. _____

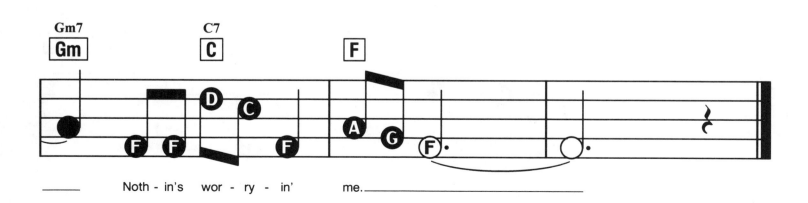

_____   Noth - in's   wor - ry - in'   me. _____

Que Sera, Sera

(Whatever Will Be, Will Be)
from THE MAN WHO KNEW TOO MUCH

Registration 10
Rhythm: Waltz

Words and Music by Jay Livingston
and Ray Evans

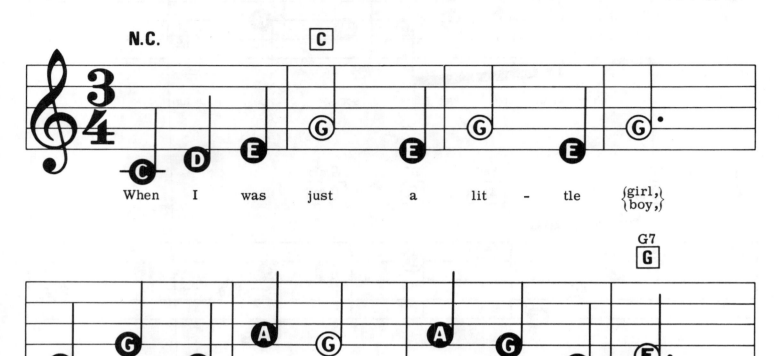

When I was just a lit - tle {girl,} {boy,}

I asked my moth - er, "What will I be? ___

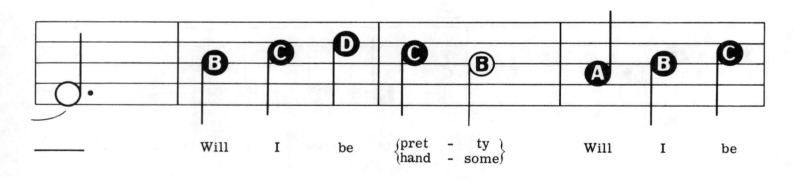

___ Will I be {pret - ty } {hand - some} Will I be

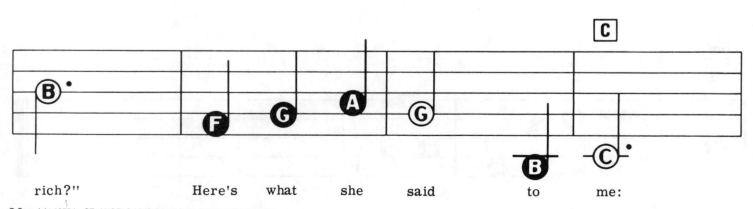

rich?" Here's what she said to me:

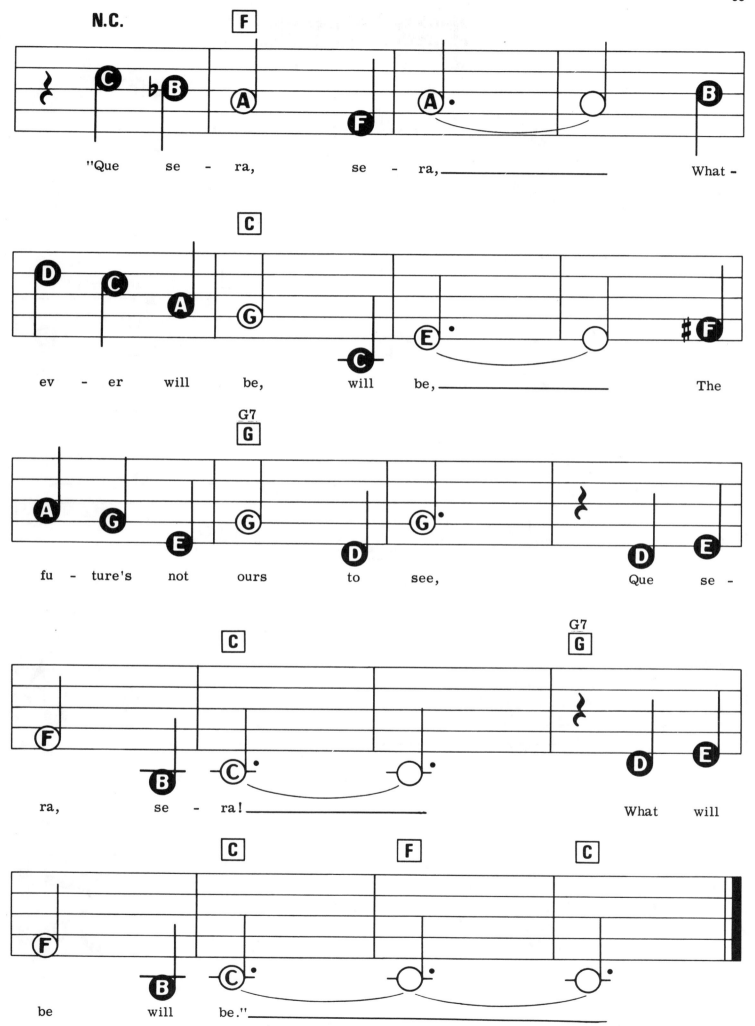

Somewhere in Time

from SOMEWHERE IN TIME

Registration 3
Rhythm: Ballad

By John Barry

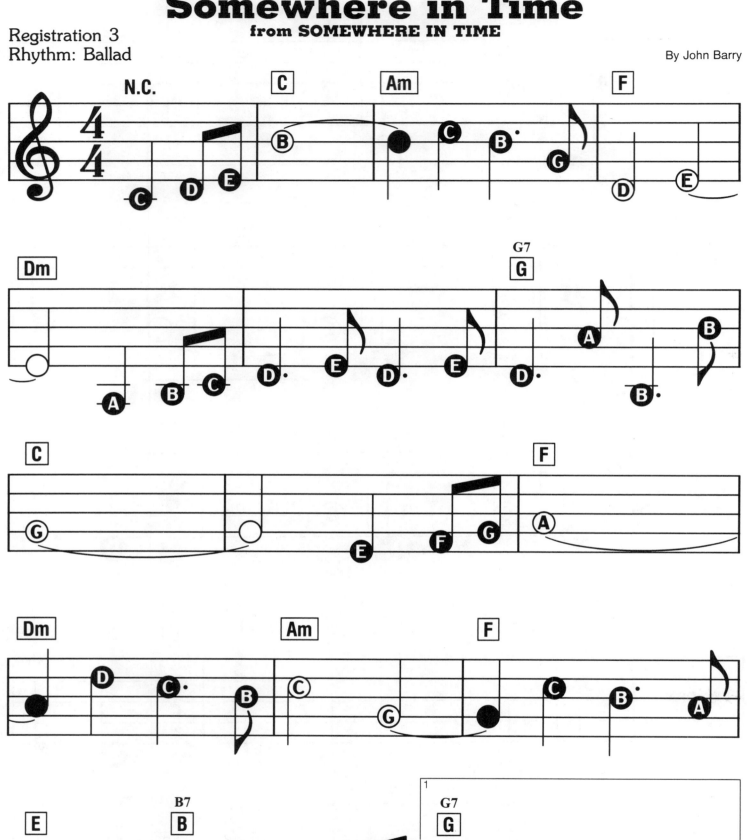

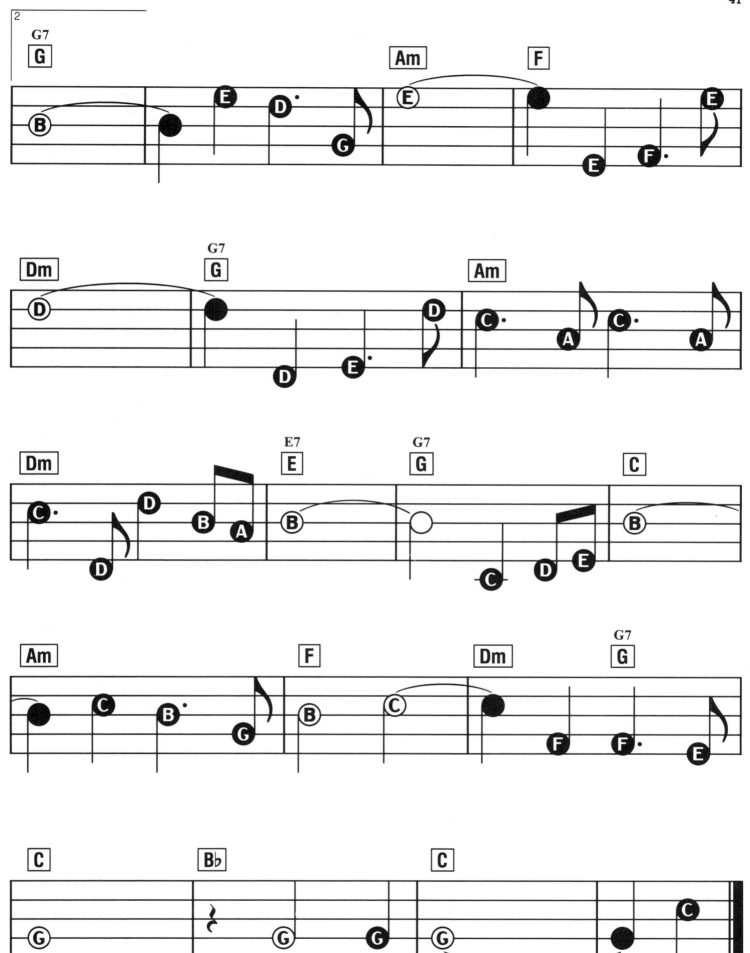

Speak Softly, Love
(Love Theme)
from the Paramount Picture THE GODFATHER

Registration 1
Rhythm: Ballad or Slow Rock

Words by Larry Kusik
Music by Nino Rota

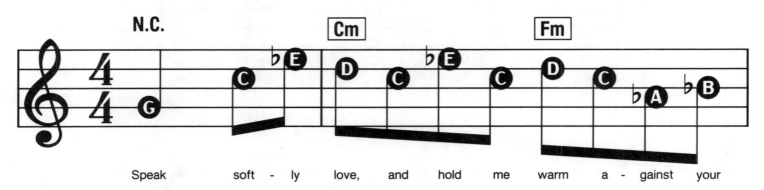

Speak soft - ly love, and hold me warm a - gainst your

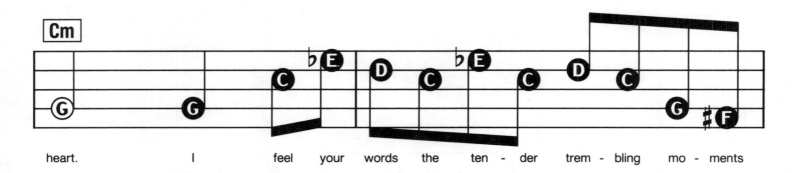

heart. I feel your words the ten - der trem - bling mo - ments

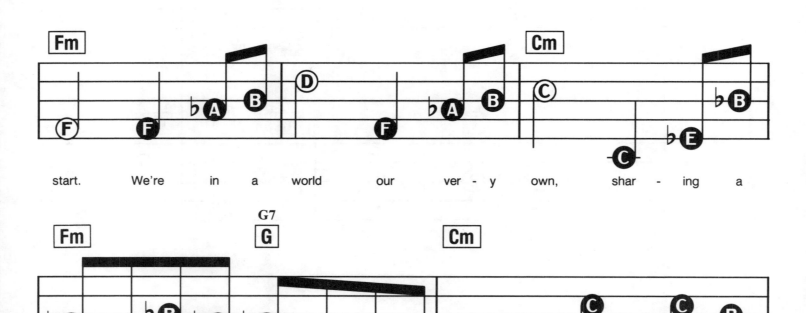

start. We're in a world our ver - y own, shar - ing a

love that on - ly few have ev - er known. Wine col - ored

43

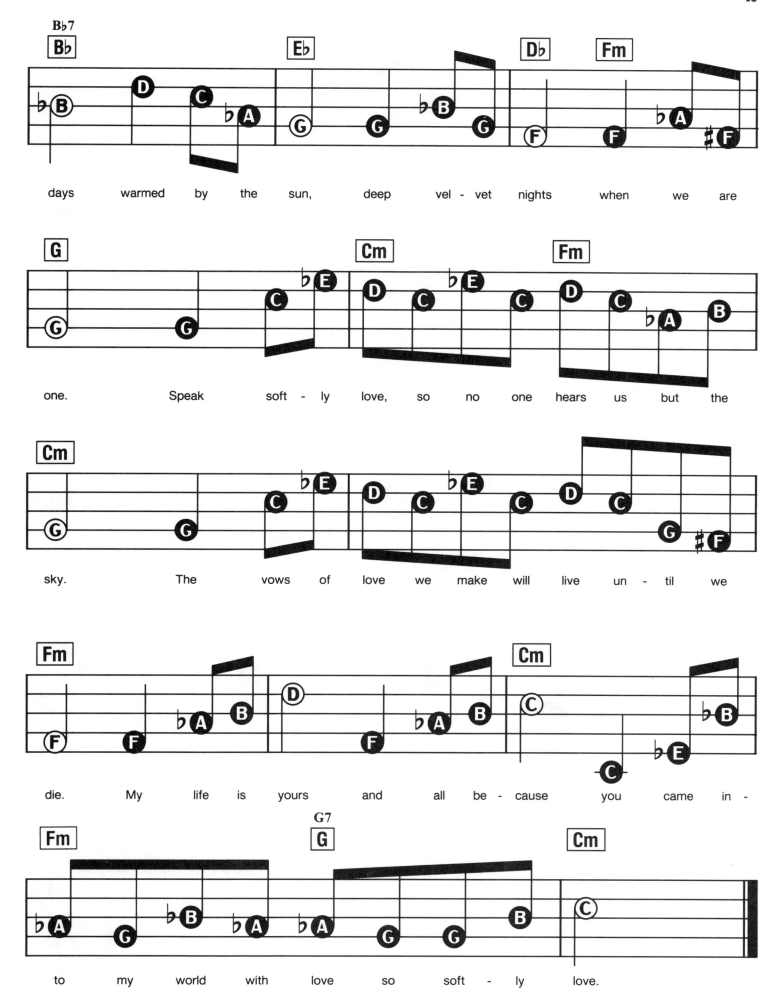

Tammy
from TAMMY AND THE BACHELOR

Registration 3
Rhythm: Waltz

Words and Music by
Jay Livingston and Ray Evans

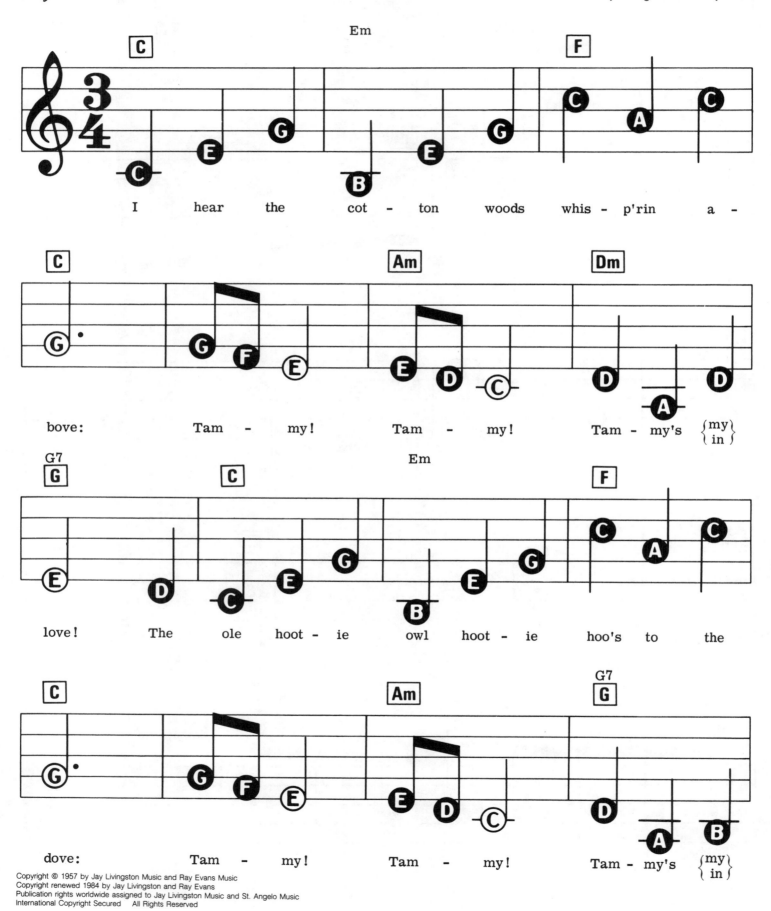

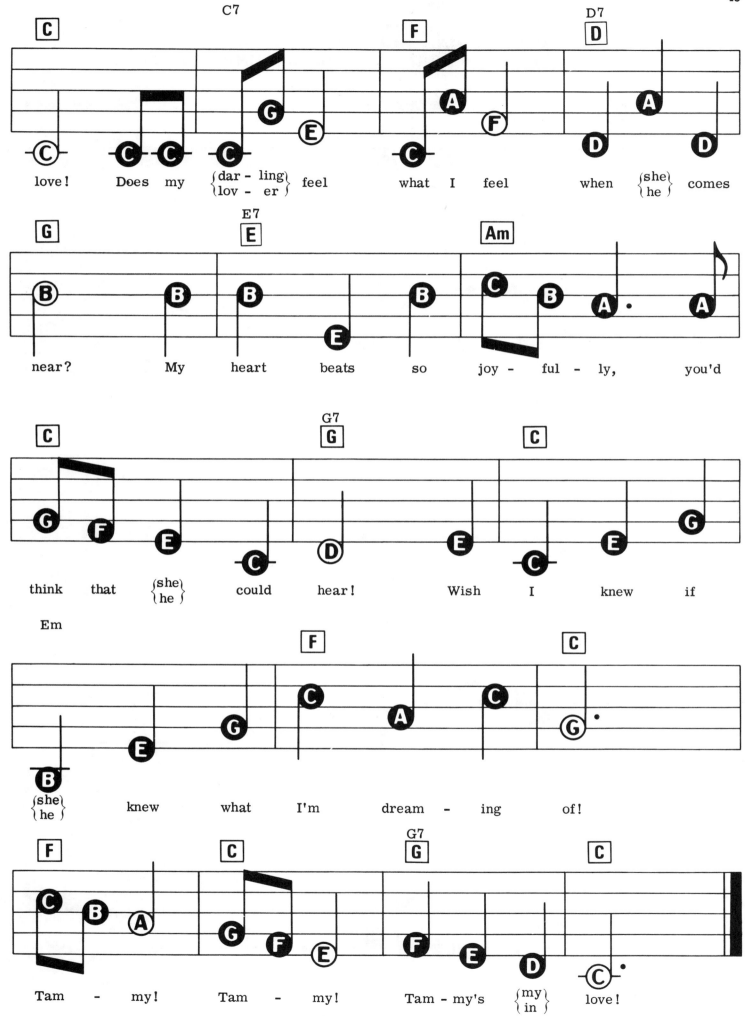

Theme from "Terms of Endearment"

Registration 9 from the Paramount Picture TERMS OF ENDEARMENT
Rhythm: Rock or 8 Beat

By Michael Gore

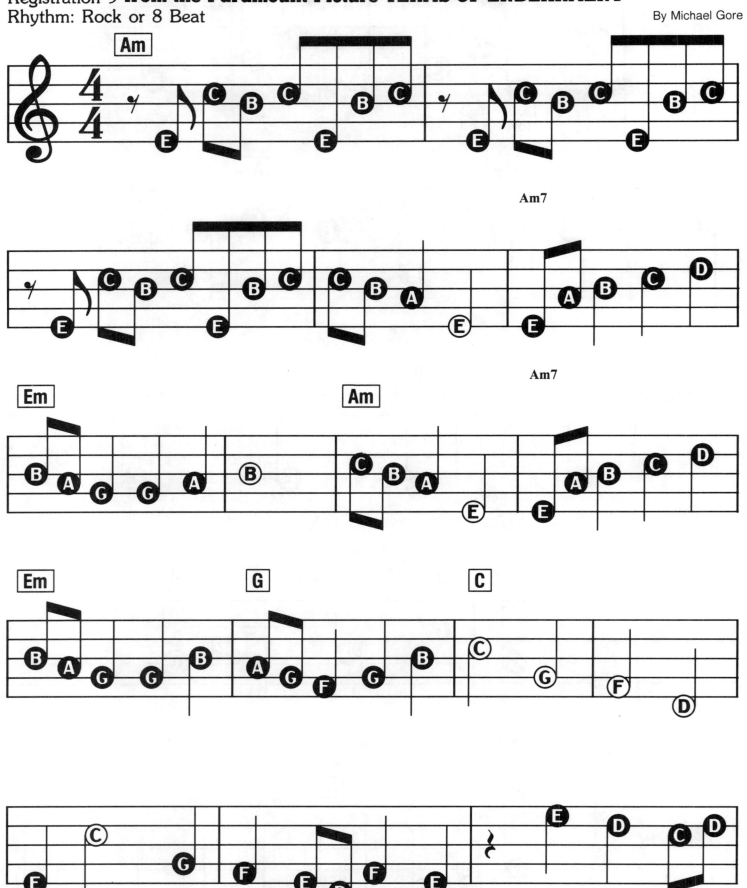

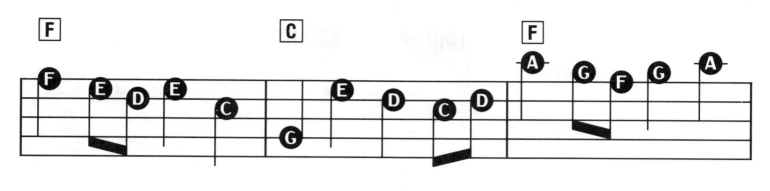
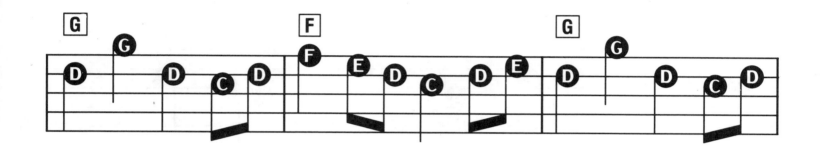
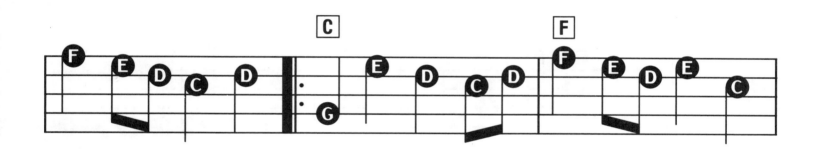
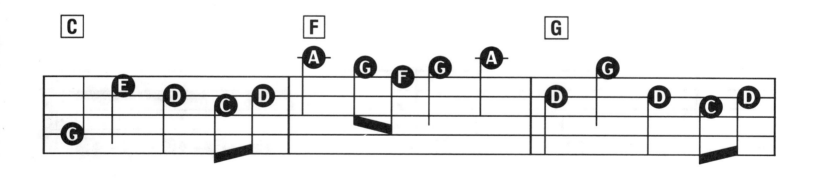
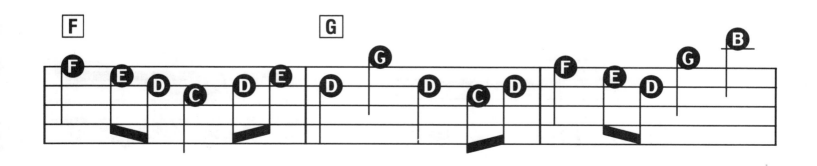

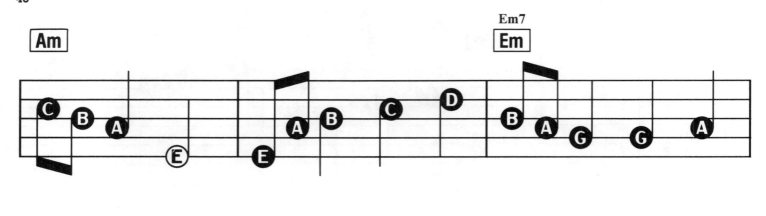

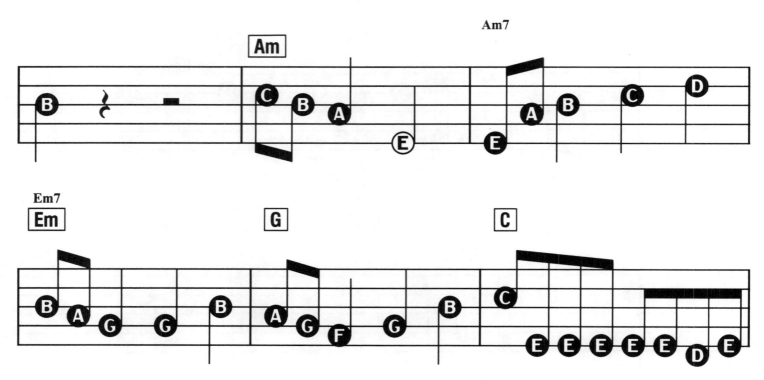

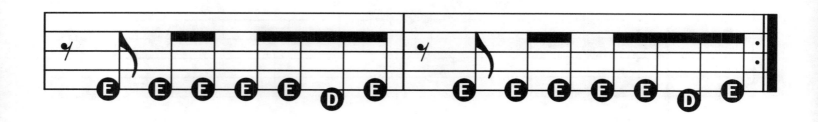

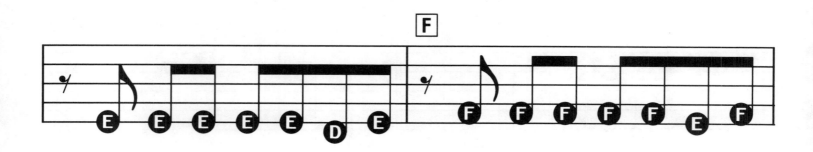

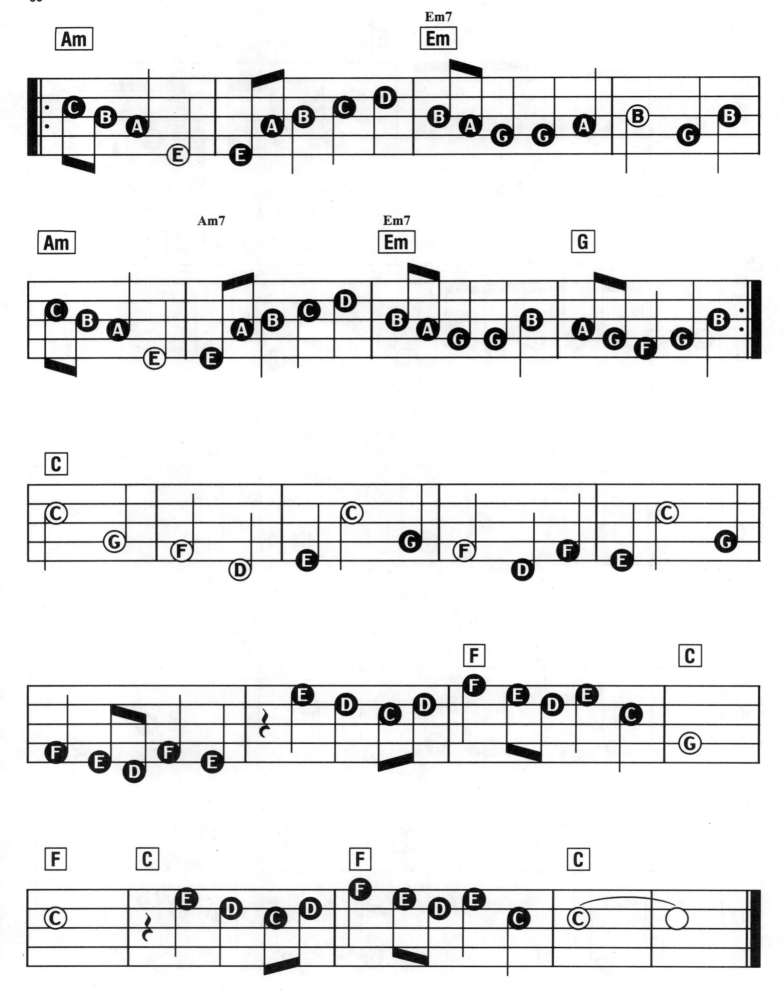

Thanks for the Memory

from the Paramount Picture BIG BROADCAST OF 1938

Registration 3
Rhythm: Swing

Words and Music by Leo Robin
and Ralph Rainger

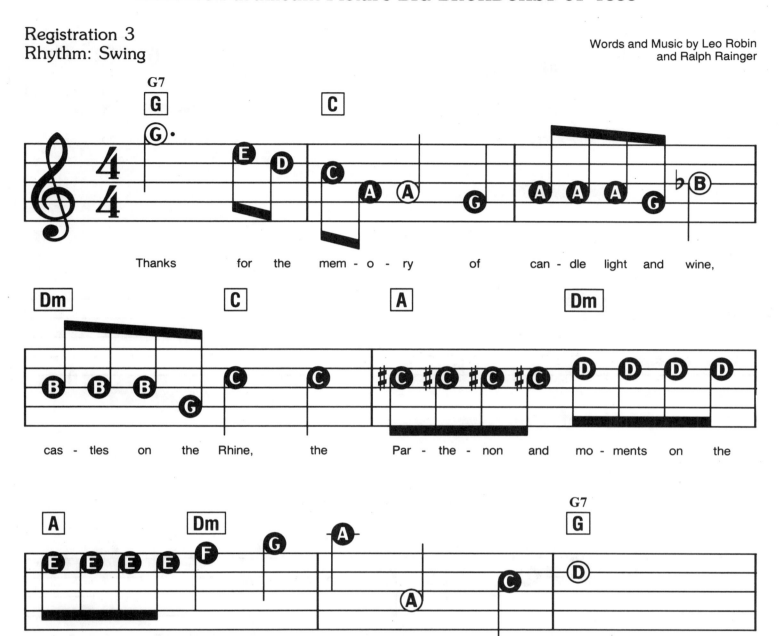

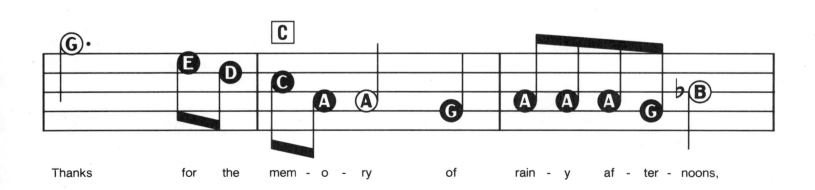

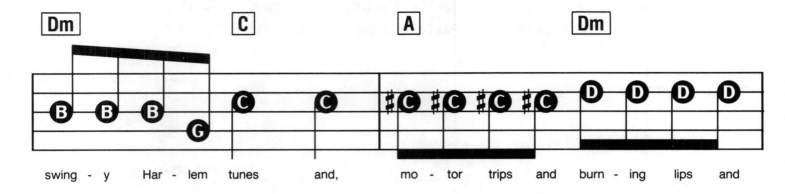

swing - y Har - lem tunes and, mo - tor trips and burn - ing lips and

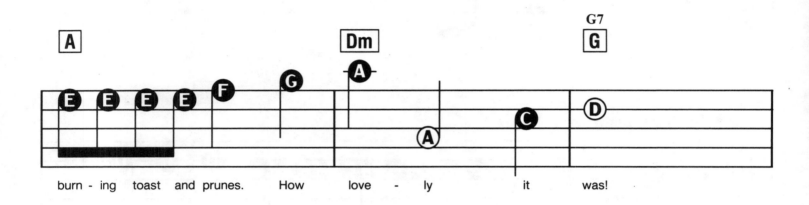

burn - ing toast and prunes. How love - ly it was!

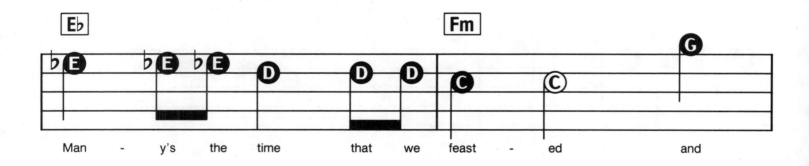

Man - y's the time that we feast - ed and

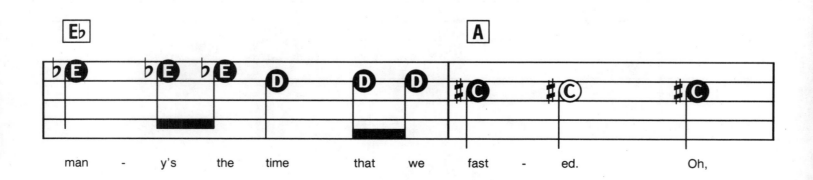

man - y's the time that we fast - ed. Oh,

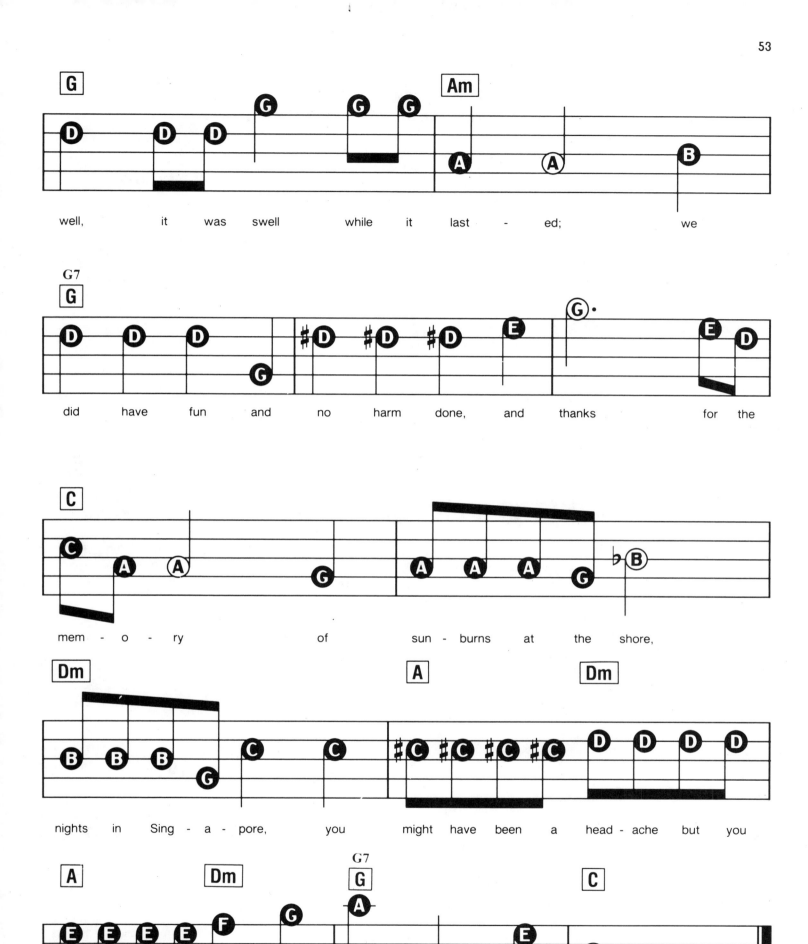

A Time for Us
(Love Theme)
from the Paramount Picture ROMEO AND JULIET

Registration 1
Rhythm: Waltz

Words by Larry Kusik and Eddie Snyder
Music by Nino Rota

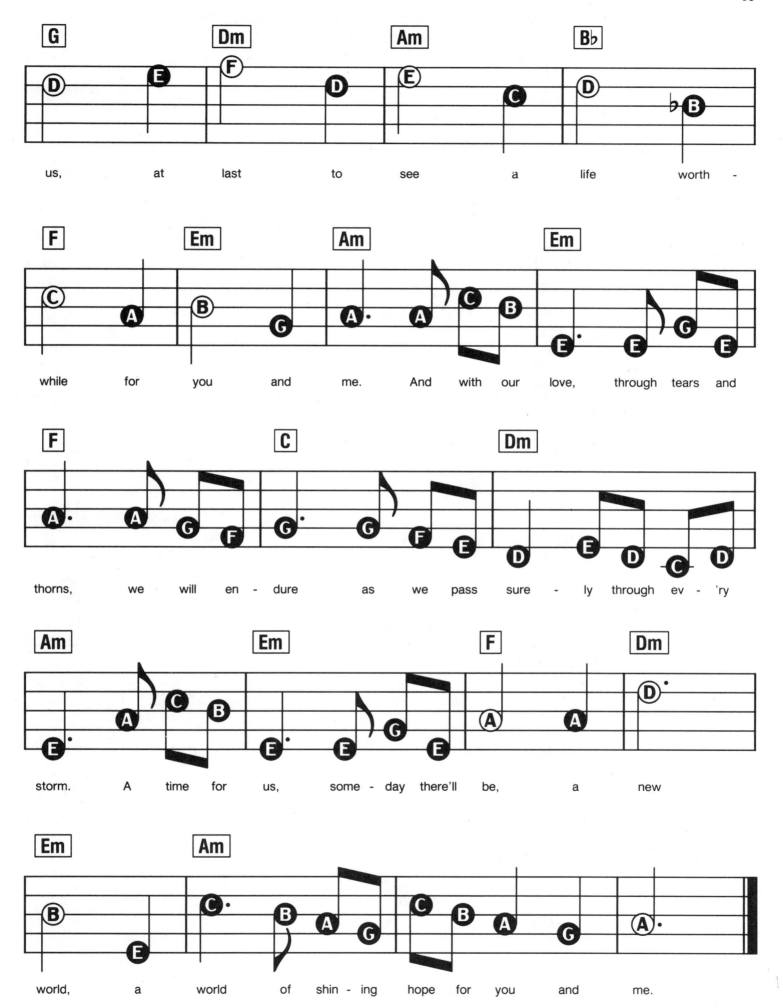

Unchained Melody
from the Motion Picture UNCHAINED
featured in the Motion Picture GHOST

Registration 4
Rhythm: Ballad

Words by Hy Zaret
Music by Alex North

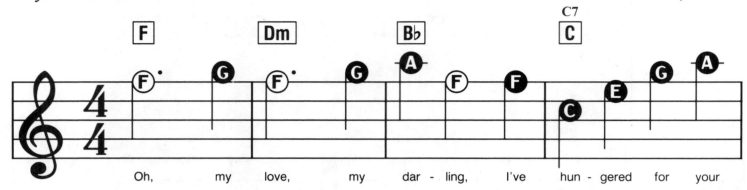

Oh, my love, my dar - ling, I've hun - gered for your

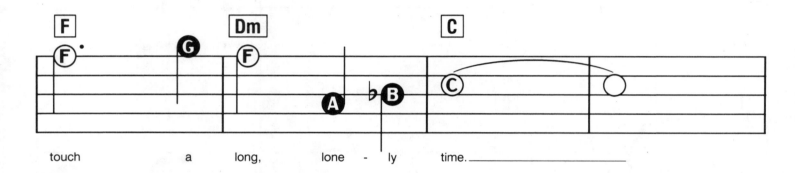

touch a long, lone - ly time._____

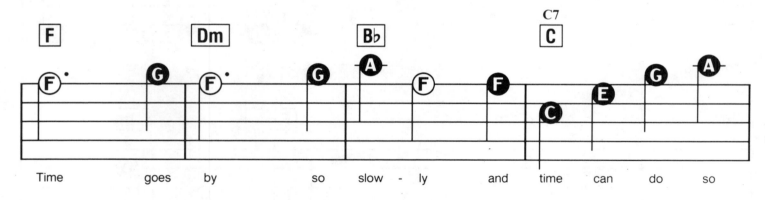

Time goes by so slow - ly and time can do so

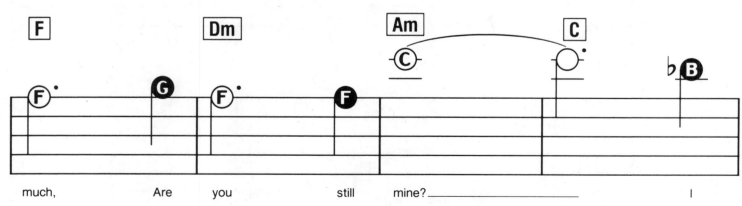

much, Are you still mine?_____

57

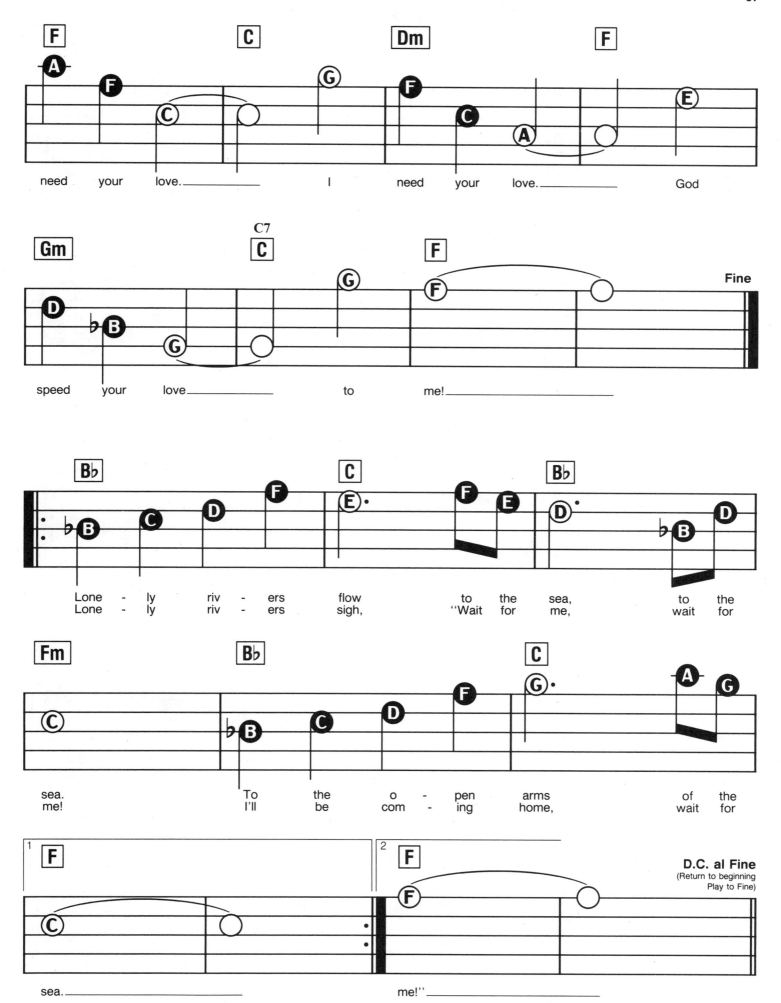

Yellow Submarine
from YELLOW SUBMARINE

Registration 2
Rhythm: 6/8 March

Words and Music by John Lennon
and Paul McCartney

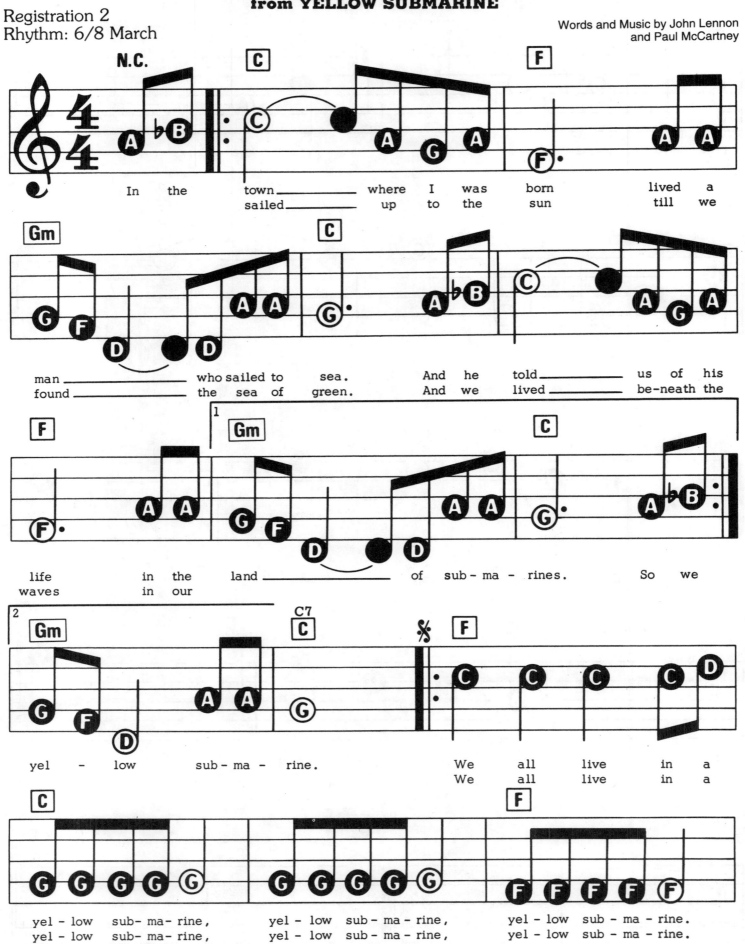

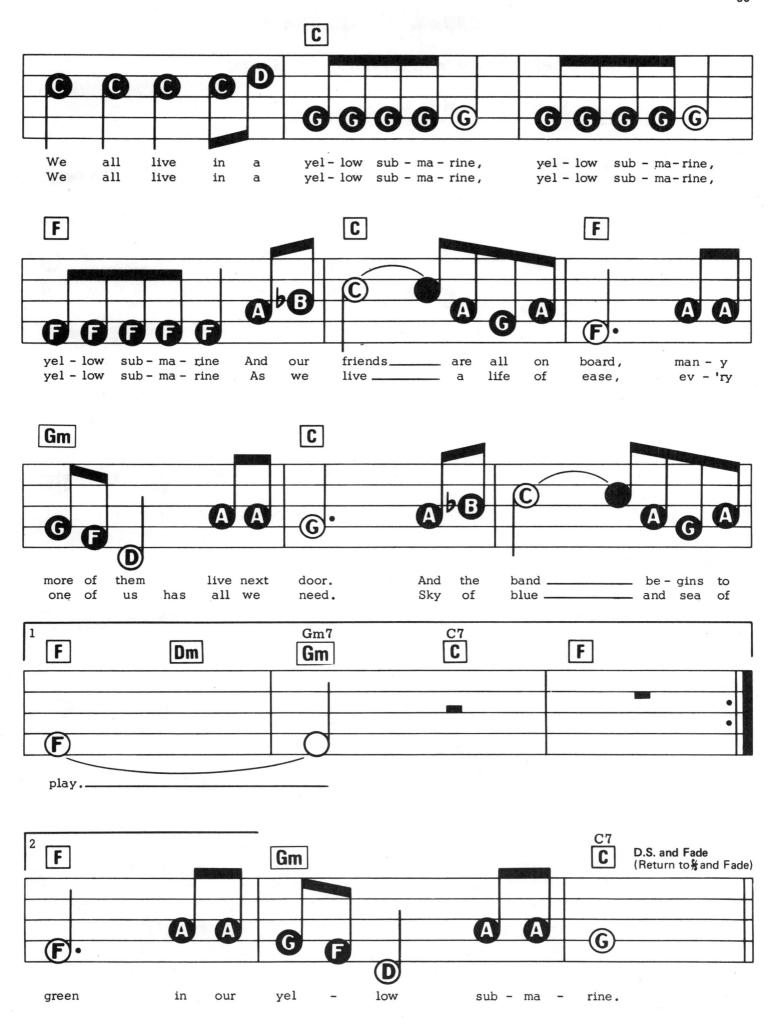

Where Do I Begin
(Love Theme)
from the Paramount Picture LOVE STORY

Registration 8
Rhythm: Ballad or Slow Rock

Words by Carl Sigman
Music by Francis Lai

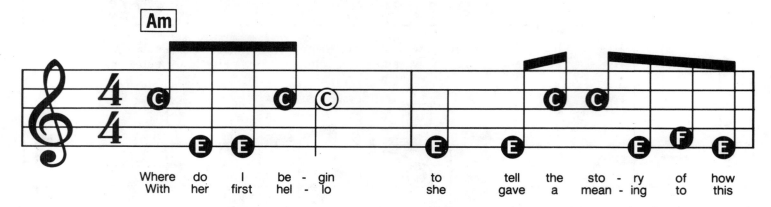

Where do I be - gin to tell the sto - ry of how
With her first hel - lo she gave a mean - ing to this

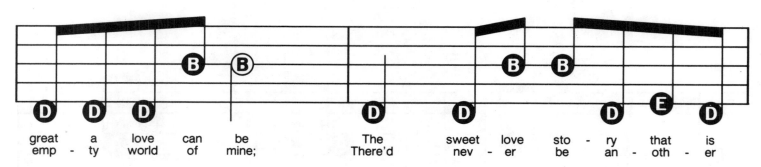

great a love can be mine; The sweet love sto - ry that is
emp - ty world of be There'd nev - er be an - oth - er

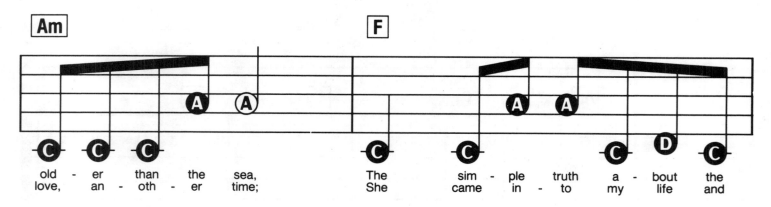

old - er than the sea, The sim - ple truth a - bout the
love, an - oth - er time; She came in - to my life and

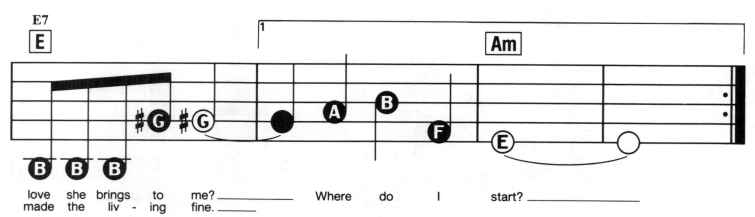

love she brings to me? Where do I start?
made the liv - ing fine.

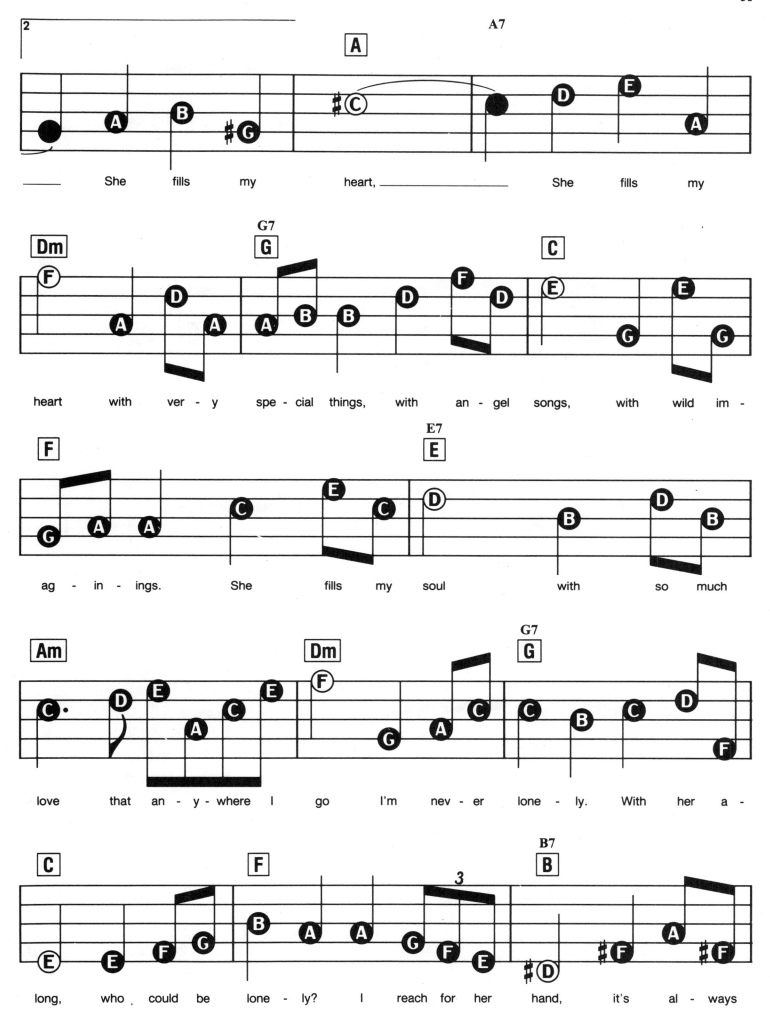

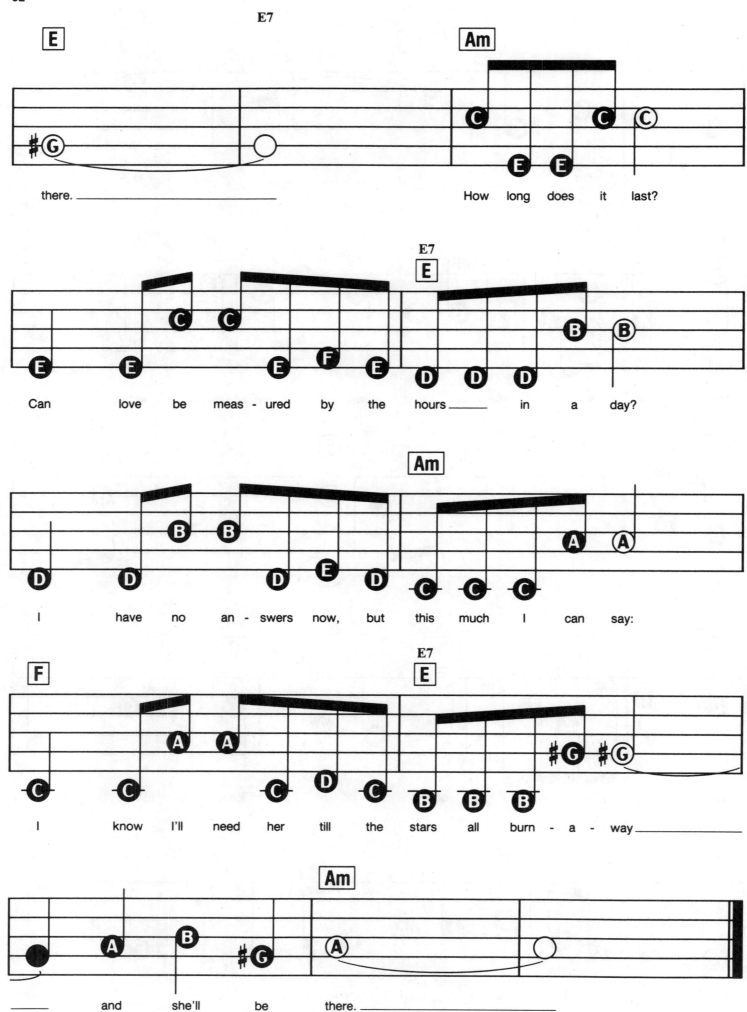

Registration Guide

- Match the Registration number on the song to the corresponding numbered category below. Select and activate an instrumental sound available on your instrument.
- Choose an automatic rhythm appropriate to the mood and style of the song. (Consult your Owner's Guide for proper operation of automatic rhythm features.)
- Adjust the tempo and volume controls to comfortable settings.

Registration

1	Flute, Pan Flute, Jazz Flute
2	Clarinet, Organ
3	Violin, Strings
4	Brass, Trumpet
5	Synth Ensemble, Accordion, Brass
6	Pipe Organ, Harpsichord
7	Jazz Organ, Vibraphone, Vibes, Electric Piano, Jazz Guitar
8	Piano, Electric Piano
9	Trumpet, Trombone, Clarinet, Saxophone, Oboe
10	Violin, Cello, Strings

MORE GREAT E-Z PLAY TODAY SONGBOOKS FOR YOUR COLLECTION

1. Love Songs
20 romantic favourites, including: Can You Feel The Love Tonight • (They Long to Be) Close to You • Have I Told You Lately • Isn't It Romantic? • Something • Through the Years • Woman • You Give Good Love • Your Song • and more.
HLE90000220

2. Broadway Favourites
21 stage songs, including: Any Dream Will Do • Climb Ev'ry Mountain • Don't Cry for Me Argentina • Getting to Know You • I Dreamed a Dream • Lambeth Walk • Memory • The Phantom of the Opera • Some Enchanted Evening • The Surrey with the Fringe on Top • and more.
HLE90000198

4. Movie Favourites
22 songs, including: Beauty and the Beast • Heart and Soul • Mona Lisa • Que Sera, Sera • Raindrops Keep Fallin' on My Head • Somewhere in Time • Speak Softly, Love • Thanks for the Memory • A Time for Us • Yellow Submarine • and more.
HLE90000210

5. Movie Greats
21 songs, including: Baby Elephant Walk • Chim Chim Cher-ee • Forrest Gump—Main Title • Isn't It Romantic? • Moon River • The Rainbow Connection • Somewhere Out There • Take My Breath Away • Up Where We Belong • A Whole New World • You Should Be Dancing • and more.
HLE90000209

6. The Decade Series — Songs of the 1920s
45 songs, including: Ain't Misbehavin' • Baby Face • Can't Help Lovin' Dat Man • Everybody Loves My Baby • A Garden in the Rain • Honeysuckle Rose • I Ain't Got Nobody • If I Had You • Louise • Me And My Shadow • Mean to Me • Miss You • More Than You Know • My Blue Heaven • Nobody Knows You When You're Down and Out • Show Me the Way to Go Home • Sunny • Who? • Why Was I Born? • You're the Cream in My Coffee • and more.
HLE090000275

7. The Decade Series — Songs of the 1930s
46 songs, including: All the Things You Are • April in Paris • Blame It on My Youth • Caravan • Cocktails for Two • A Fine Romance • Heart and Soul • I Can't Get Started with You • I'm Gonna Sit Right Down and Write Myself a Letter • In a Sentimental Mood • Isn't It Romantic? • Lambeth Walk • Moonglow • My Romance • Pennies from Heaven • Smoke Gets in Your Eyes • Thanks for the Memory • The Touch of Your Lips • The Very Thought of You • The Way You Look Tonight • and more.
HLE90000286

8. The Decade Series — Songs of the 1940s
Over 40 songs, including: All Through the Day • Anniversary Song • Baby, It's Cold Outside • Besame Mucho • Blue Champagne • Boogie Woogie Bugle Boy • Diamonds Are a Girl's Best Friend • Don't Get Around Much Anymore • Have I Told You Lately That I Love You • I'll Remember April • I've Got a Lovely Bunch of Cocoanuts • It Might As Well Be Spring • It's a Grand Night for Singing • The Last Time I Saw Paris • Mairzy Doats • The Nearness of You • Oklahoma • People Will Say We're in Love • Take the "A" Train • Tangerine • Tuxedo Junction • You'll Never Walk Alone • and more.
HLE90000297

9. The Decade Series — Songs of the 1950s
52 songs, including: All Shook Up • Angel Eyes • Arrivederci Roma • Blue Velvet • Chantilly Lace • Climb Ev'ry Mountain • Cry Me A River • Fly Me To The Moon • Johnny B. Goode • Let It Be Me • Luck Be a Lady • Misty • Mona Lisa • Only You (And You Alone) • Peggy Sue • Que Sera, Sera • Rock Around the Clock • Satin Doll • That'll Be the Day • Three Coins in the Fountain • Tutti Fruitti • Unchained Melody • Witchcraft • and more.
HLE90000308

10. The Decade Series — Songs of the 1960s
49 songs, including: Alfie • Bluesette • Bridge Over Troubled Water • Can't Help Falling In Love • Crazy • Crying • Eleanor Rigby • The Girl from Ipanema • Here, There and Everywhere • If I Had a Hammer • King of the Road • Leaving on a Jet Plane • Light My Fire • The Lion Sleeps Tonight • A Man and a Woman • Moon River • Raindrops Keep Fallin' on My Head • The Shadow of Your Smile • Something • Summer Samba (So Nice) • Those Were the Days • A Time for Us • Twist and Shout • and more.
HLE90000319

11. The Decade Series — Songs of the 1970s
39 songs, including: The Air That I Breathe • Annie's Song • Band on the Run • The Candy Man • (They Long to Be) Close to You • Copacabana • Crocodile Rock • Dancing Queen • Don't Cry for Me Argentina • How Deep Is Your Love • I Don't Know How to Love Him • Imagine • Killing Me Softly with His Song • Let It Be • Maybe I'm Amazed • Nights in White Satin • Rocket Man • Sometimes When We Touch • You Don't Bring Me Flowers • You Light Up My Life • and more.
HLE90000320

12. The Decade Series — Songs of the 1980s
36 songs, including: Addicted to Love • Against All Odds • All I Ask of You • All Out of Love • Axel F • Candle in the Wind • Don't Worry, Be Happy • Ebony and Ivory • Every Breath You Take • Hard Habit to Break • I Dreamed a Dream • Longer • Love Changes Everything • Memory • Sailing • Somewhere Out There • Sweet Dreams (Are Made Of This) • Take My Breath Away • Up Where We Belong • What's Love Got to Do With It • The Wind Beneath My Wings • With or Without You • and more.
HLE90000330

13. The Decade Series: Songs of the 1990s
33 songs, including: All for Love • Always • Always Be My Baby • Circle of Life • Common People • Father and Son • Fields of Gold • Hero • I Found Someone • Mission: Impossible Theme • No More "I Love You's" • Save the Best for Last • Tears in Heaven • Unchained Melody • A Whole New World • With One Look • Wonderwall • You Are Not Alone • and more.
HLE90000341

14. Imagine
29 songs for a better world, including: All You Need Is Love • Circle of Life • Colors of the Wind • From a Distance • God Help the Outcasts • If I Had a Hammer • Imagine • The Impossible Dream • The Power of the Dream • Someday • Turn! Turn! Turn! • What the World Needs Now Is Love • With a Little Help from My Friends • and more.
HLE90000253

15. All You Need Is Love
31 classics from the hip years of the late 60s and early 70s, including: All You Need Is Love • Blowin' in the Wind • Born to Be Wild • Bridge Over Troubled Water • Hey Joe • Imagine • Light My Fire • Love Her Madly • Magic Carpet Ride • Mr. Tambourine Man • My Generation • Riders on the Storm • The Sounds of Silence • Turn! Turn! Turn! • A Whiter Shade of Pale • and more.
HLE90000264

16. Broadway Greats
23 songs, including: All I Ask of You • Consider Yourself • Edelweiss • Love Changes Everything • Ol' Man River • On My Own • The Sound of Music • Sun and Moon • Unexpected Song • We Kiss in a Shadow • Younger Than Springtime • and more.
HLE90000187

HAL LEONARD EUROPE
DISTRIBUTED BY MUSIC SALES